ANYONE FOR TENORS?

BY THE SAME AUTHOR

The Selsey Tram
Six Of The Best
The Jennings Companion
Financial Penalties
Around Chichester In Old Photographs
Here's A Pretty Mess!
Magisterial Lore
The Beaten Track (republished as *The Big Walks Of Great Britain)*
Poetic Justice
That's My Girl
Walking The Coastline Of Sussex
Best Sussex Walks
Let's Take It From The Top
Walking The Disused Railways Of Sussex
Once More From The Top
Sussex Top Tens
Walking The Kent Coast From End To End
Walking The Riversides Of Sussex
Walking The South Coast Of England

ABOUT THE CHARITIES

The Sussex Snowdrop Trust (registered charity 1096622) was set up to provide help for families in Sussex with children suffering from life-threatening or life-limiting illnesses, giving financial assistance to affected families, providing practical care and compassionate support, and supplying specialist equipment to meet the day-to-day needs of the children.

Children On The Edge (registered charity 1101441) is based in Chichester in West Sussex but provides support to children who are suffering all around the world. Recent projects include aid to cyclone victims in Burma, the provision of food and education to children in East Timor, and help for children and families still affected by the tsunami in south-east Asia in 2004.

All profits raised from sales of this book will be donated to these charities.

ANYONE FOR TENORS?

By DAVID BATHURST

Illustrated by TERENCE WHITLOCK

Romansmead Publications

First published in 2008 by

Romansmead Publications
6 Woodgate Close
Woodgate
Chichester
West Sussex PO20 3TA

Printed in England by CPI Antony Rowe, Bumpers Farm, Chippenham Wiltshire SN14 6LH

British Library Cataloguing-in-Publication Data.
A catalogue record for this book is available from the British Library.

ISBN 978-0-9523936-9-6

PROLOGUE

Monday 31st December

Dear Jackie,

Looking through my old correspondence last night, I couldn't believe it was four whole years since I last wrote to you. It was great to receive your Christmas card and I'm really pleased things have worked out so well for you in New Zealand. I only hope this letter gets to you okay. When Katie suggested a cheap alternative to buying Christmas present labels, it never occurred to me that this would involve hacking half of my Christmas cards to pieces including the one with your address on it. Still, I've always enjoyed jigsaw puzzles and I'm sure there's a psychotherapist somewhere who'd see the healing potential in an evening's examination of the contents of a study waste bin sifting out fragments of stiff paper wishing the recipient an Erry Rist and Shes for a Py New Ear.

As you will see from our address, Katie and I have moved. I recently secured a promotion at work which meant a change of office location to the larger town of Dellford. Unfortunately the commute from our old house, while still theoretically doable each day, soon became intolerable in practice. Twenty-four miles each way may not seem excessive, but I have always liked to be within walking or cycling distance of my work, and with that in mind we decided to move to Lambsball Green, a large village which lies just a short bike ride from my new office in Dellford. We finally completed on our house move at the beginning of December. Although I could have decided to keep up my membership of the choir of St Basil's, our old church, I was only too pleased to have a pretext for getting out of it while I still had some vestiges of sanity left in me. What was once a thriving choir is now almost pitiful in terms of both size and levels of musical competence, with so many loyal singers now no longer involved. Brian and Rachel Ellis, two lovely people who have always been so friendly and hospitable towards me, had what they described to me as an "awesome spiritual revelation" in the form of an episode of *A Place In The Sun* they happened to see one Monday teatime on Channel Four, and as a result they decided to move to a villa in the south of France, never to darken the doors of St Basil's again. Although Katie probably wouldn't thank me for saying it, I was extremely sad when Lesley Markwick left to live in North Yorkshire, taking with her her beautiful daughter Jane. With her stunning good looks, dazzling dress sense and effusive outgoing personality, Jane had for a long time exercised a mesmeric hold over me, despite the fact that in trying to establish a relationship with her I'd been stood up more times than Subbuteo table football men on the deck of a cruise ship during a force 10 gale. Irvng Cattermole, a laconic individual but a very useful singer, suddenly one day asked himself why he was sitting in church when UK Gold had just started a Sunday morning series of re-runs of *The Six Million Dollar Man*, walked out on the vicar's versicles and never returned. Ken Foulkes, having suffered a major heart attack the year before last, had to withdraw from all his singing commitments and although he attends church from time to time, it is to exercise a different albeit highly useful function by being the only member of the congregation actually to attempt to sing any of the hymns in tune. Sadly Eileen Crosby recently departed to the "great parish choir in the sky," as the choirmaster Frank Tripplehorn sensitively announced her death in the middle of choir practice last July, sandwiched in between announcements of the choir's lingerie stall at the summer bazaar and the choir's late summer outing to Pontins at Birchington-on-Sea. And Ruth Hartnell, who had been hugely helpful to me in a number of fundraising initiatives, finally resigned from the ranks as a result of the recruitment into the choir of Sylvia Faraday, to whom Ruth refuses to speak, apparently as a result of allegations of sharp practice in the church Sports Day egg and spoon race in 1974. Some efforts have been made to replace the lost singers, but these haven't met with unqualified success. Take Megan Kilshaw, for instance. She nodded vigorously and punched the air with delight when I asked her if she'd like to join the choir, and has an infectious smile and unbridled enthusiasm for everything she does, but I guess that her command of the rudiments of music may be somewhat lacking at the age of 23 months. I can think of several people who, if I asked them, would join the choir, but since the arrival of any of them would result in the resignation of half the existing membership, the choir would be no better off, and probably rather worse off, than before. And there are one or two members of the congregation who have kindly told me they would be happy to consider joining, which would be fine had not Frank Tripplehorn assured me that given the choice between recruiting them and spending every Sunday morning for the rest of his days offering monolingual migrant Romanian labourers conducted tours of the public conveniences of Bournemouth he would be on his way to foreign language night school that very same evening.

It's certainly nice to have got out of my St Basil's rut, and good to be so close to my work again, but having devoted so much of my leisure time to musical activity, both sacred and secular, over the past couple of years, I am disappointed to see how little opportunity there is for either in our new village. Although it is a large and indeed growing community, there's no choral society, nor an amateur dramatic or operatic society, and the village church of St Augustine of Hippo which we've attended on a few Sundays seems very sterile. At a recent act of worship, it seems that some research was undertaken and it was ascertained that of a congregation of just 37 people, the youngest member of the congregation was 56 and more than half were over 85. And this was billed as a Youth Service. It doesn't help that the vicar has been away for a few months, firstly having an operation and then on sabbatical lasting till the spring, and during the few weeks we've been coming to the church we have had the dubious privilege of a succession of celebrants who present the most cogent argument I have yet met for compulsory retirement from all priestly duties at the age of 140. It was my concern at the lack of dynamism in our new church, combined with a wish to put something really constructive into village life and my love for a challenge, which led me to conceive an Idea. It came to me during the midnight service at the church, when the presence of a number of sons and daughters of regular worshippers, back with their parents for Christmas, brought the average age of the congregation for a service other than a wedding down to below 70 for the first time since....the last midnight service. Midnight services seem to be big life-changing experiences for me. It had been immediately after the midnight service five years ago that my relationship with Katie had effectively begun, with a tender kiss beside the Christmas crib beneath the soft shine of the stars through the south window. Exactly a year later, again following the service, we had made our way out of church together and pledged ourselves to each other for life under the clear moonlit skies. And at last year's service, I was informed that as the booby prize winner for the fewest correct entries in the church baby photo competition, I was now the proud owner of an inflatable snowman. At this year's midnight service, I decided that by this time next year, our village will have its very own singing group. It will be open to all, the only stipulations being that all members must be residents of the village and able both to sing in tune and blend with other singers. The aims of the group will be to provide entertainment for the local community, opportunities for young ambitious singers, and good choral backing for the "bigger" services at the church. I purposely don't want to form a church choir as such; I'm anxious not to deter any would-be singers who the moment the words "church choir" are mentioned immediately think of mildewed cassocks, half-consumed packs of Lockets, dreary Victorian psalm chants composed by long-suffering conductors of under-achieving Victorian church choirs, and Friday nights in the company of 92-year-old spinsters most of whom could claim no more significant a contribution to church musical life than the administration of a clip round the ear to the choirboy caught with a Yorkie in his Nunc Dimittis.

If you'll forgive a management cliché, I'm starting with a blank sheet of paper. After four weeks here, Katie and I still know absolutely nobody in Lambsball Green. Our neighbours keep themselves to themselves, and the only people in the church congregation who have deigned to speak to us live in the town or neighbouring villages. The guy who serves me in the village shop is always extremely charming, polite and courteous, but it's hard to get to know him well all the time he is unable, as a Latvian national, to speak a word of English. The middle-aged man four doors down from us did call round soon after we moved in and talked with us for more than two hours, asking us at length about our health and our future plans, and we would have been quite touched by his concern for us had he not been doing it for the purpose of selling critical illness insurance. And while it was a pleasure to note that the village is blessed with many young people boasting a refreshingly vibrant, enthusiastic and uninhibited outlook on life, I would rather this were channelled into something other than re-enacting the previous day's Premiership football action using the dustbins at number 27 as goalposts at two o'clock in the morning. There have been times since the midnight service when I've wondered if the whole thing is just too ridiculous and whether I'd be better off getting involved in music-making activities in Dellford instead, and I spent much of last night on the phone to some of my former associates at St Basil's seeking their reassurance and advice. Ruth Hartnell said that I certainly had the necessary positive attitude combined with organisational skills and the only way that I would know if it was worth it was by trying it. Margaret Pardew, whose depth of faith and commitment puts mine to shame, told me that she was sure that our loving Father had it all in hand, and that if I laid my plans before Him in prayer and entrusted Him with them, they would yield fruit beyond my fondest imaginings. And Frank Tripplehorn told me I was two scoops short of a tub of chocolate nut sundae and how could I consider dragging the local populace from their armchairs with the new series of *Strictly Come Dishwashing* about to start on Channel 5.

Paradoxically, perhaps, it was my former choirmaster's negativity about the project that erased my doubts and made me even more determined to see it through. My next phone call was to book the village Assembly Room for an inaugural meeting on January 17th giving me two and a half weeks for us to organise publicity and awaken some interest. At that meeting I'm hopeful that I can at least see what musical talent exists in Lambsball Green and how it can best be used to enrich the local community, bolster the flagging fortunes of the church of St Augustine of Hippo, and also generate funds to support charities both at home and abroad. From tomorrow, New Year's Day, when work starts in earnest,

I'm keen to keep a diary of how I get on, not only to keep you informed but also in the hope that it may help others who feel moved to do something similar to learn from my mistakes and to draw inspiration from what I hope and pray will be a successful venture. But at least if I fail, I can give some thought to adopting Irving Cattermole's suggestion as to a far more realistic and achievable means of impacting in a positive, constructive and life-enhancing fashion upon those around me. By setting up in business flogging beach balls, inflatable rubber dinghies, Kiss Me Quick hats and shrimping nets from the railway station car park, Dusty City, Central African Republic.

JANUARY

Tuesday 1st January

Decided it would be nice to celebrate the start of another year with a drink at the village pub, the Welldiggers Arms. We arrived at midday and found the main bar was predictably fairly busy, with not a seat to be had, while singing was heard to be emanating from the lounge bar. On the basis that if we had to stay standing to enjoy our New Year drinks, we might as well be entertained in the process, we adjourned to the lounge bar and were treated to what was a more than acceptable rendition of the *Skye Boat Song* from four young men dressed in kilts. Sensing possible recruits for the singing group, I waited till they had finished then as the applause died down I went up to the youngest and hairiest of the four and told him how much I'd enjoyed the impromptu Hogmanay celebration.

"Oh, that's only the warm-up to the main event," he replied in broad Cockney. "Half twelve, we all go outside for a New Year dip. Come and join us if you like."

"I'm afraid I've not got my swimming costume," I replied.

"It's not a swim," explained one of his colleagues, who judging by his accent also did not appear to boast roots going any further north than Brent Cross Shopping Centre. "At 12.30 we take off our shoes and socks and do a conga through the fish pond behind the pub. Whoever does it is entitled to membership of the Lambsball Green Dippers." And one of the other two members of the quartet, who introduced himself to me as Barney, put down his glass of beer and proceeded to talk me through the not inconsiderable list of entitlements that such membership carried.

Though dubious at first, I was won over by a large brandy and the prospect of friendship with four very good singers, even though I was left with precious little idea of what the rationale behind, and the functions of, the Lambsball Green Dippers were actually supposed to be. It was clear that fish were involved somewhere, but beyond the fact that a certain amount of tradition and ritual was involved, some of which seemed to have almost Masonic overtones, I could not be certain about anything more. Anyway, I couldn't fault their hospitality, and by the time the hand of the lounge bar clock had reached twenty-eight minutes past, I was actually quite looking forward to the whole thing, and not as unnerved as I perhaps might have been by the fact that almost everybody in both bars was making their way out to view the spectacle. Some even had their mobile phone cameras poised to record it. And I can only think it was the second brandy that was thrust into my hand shortly before the event that robbed me of any inhibitions I had about being entrusted with leadership of the conga procession out of the back door of the pub to the strains of *Auld Lang Syne*. Seeing the murky pool just beyond an area of seating to the right, I veered sharply in that direction and, taking the yells from behind me as shouts of encouragement, I jumped in. But instead of making contact with the bottom of the pond at just above ankle depth, as I had been assured I would do, I found my whole brandy-fuelled body disappearing into a spectacularly watery abyss, soaking every part of me from the tips of my toes to the hairs on my head. Never a keen swimmer and reliant for my survival in these desperate circumstances on the little I recalled from the formidable Commander Nettlefield's third form swimming lessons, I somehow fought my way back to the surface and dragged myself onto the patio, aware not only that water was dripping from each fold of my now ruined jumper but my hair was coated with a glutinous yellow substance that could either have been rotting fish food or a regurgitated portion of dodgy prawn biryani. To make matters worse, I was greeted by hysterical laughter from the assembled Welldiggers Arms patrons, as well as a multitude of fingers pointing in the direction of the conga procession which had found its way to and was splashing in carefree fashion in a second and evidently far shallower pond at the bottom of the garden.

As I stood impotently in the distinctly chilly January air, Barney abandoned his beery frolics and came hurrying up to me. I noticed him grimace the moment he came near me, suggesting that water was definitely only one, and emphatically the most innocuous, of the various liquids in which I had just immersed myself. "We said the fish pond, not the old well," he pointed out. "But we've had a brief committee meeting and decided to let you in the Dippers anyway."

As I staggered home, my teeth chattering, and my antics now undoubtedly destined for a Saturday night camcorder bloopers TV date with Harry Hill or one of his infamous successors, I could at least console myself with two things. First, that if I ever wish to join the Baptists, I will already have one of the principal credentials. And secondly, that I can now look forward to the benefits that membership of the Dippers will bring. A shark-shaped membership badge, a voucher entitling me to a free packet of Birds Eye cod in batter, and, when I'm next in Dellford, a five per cent discount off the purchase of a goldfish from Barney's brother's cut-price aquatic pet store. Tanks For Nothing.

Thursday 3rd January

I decided on a rather drier means of promoting the inaugural meeting today, namely by way of contributing an article to the *Dellford Chronicle*. I telephoned the editorial department and was advised to send an email which I duly did – three times – but without getting any response at all despite giving my email, land line, mobile and fax number and having been promised an instant acknowledgement. After more than three hours of infuriating non-response, I rang the editorial department again and enquired what was going on. I was asked to hold, and five minutes later found myself speaking to someone called Karl, who in fairness to him apologised for keeping me waiting and asked what he could do for me. I gave what I thought was an excellent plug for the 17th event, explaining what I was seeking to achieve, and how good it would be for the community if it worked. "That sounds great," Karl said when I finished. "I'm sure the editorial team would be most interested. Just pop all that to them in an email."

Having squeezed another cubic metre of gunge from my squidgy stress reliever, I decided to devote my lunch hour to going round to their offices in person and venting my frustrations on the hapless greying man in the reception area.

"I mean," I said, having told him the whole sorry story, "what do I have to do to get myself mentioned in your paper?"

"Okay, let's think about this," said the greying man. "Did you get a mention in the New Year's Honours List?"

"Not to my knowledge," I replied.

"Have you raised £5000 towards the new kidney unit in Dellford General Hospital?"

"Sadly I can't say I have," I replied.

"Have you parachuted off the weather-vane of the Canfield Road Retail Park Asda while peeling a ripe banana?"

"Only after a very good lunch," I quipped. "And I don't get many of those."

"In that case you've no chance," he said. "Your best bet's to get hold of Angus Spadgwick and ask him to include it in the Lambsball Green column in the Village Correspondents' page. I think I've got his details here." He rummaged in a pile of papers on the desk and moments later was handing me a sheet with Mr Spadgwick's address and phone number. "That's probably the most you can hope for," he went on, "what with this big news story occupying so many column inches. But I expect you know about that."

I told him I didn't.

"It's a biggie," he told me. "Proposals to convert the old church at the bottom of Edward Street into a betting shop."

"Well, one can understand people getting upset about things like that," I said. "Places of worship and sanctuary, houses of God, being turned into gambling dens promoting greed and adding to the social problems of the area and moral bankruptcy of our nation. When did the church actually close?"

"I think it was in 1787," he replied.

Resigning myself to three lines at the bottom of page sixty-eight of the second supplement, I thanked him very much for his time, his valuable help and his very candid appraisal of my chances of being included in the paper.
"By the way," I said, as I was leaving, "what is your job here?" "Oh, I don't work here," he told me. "I just came in to mend the fax machine."

Sunday 6th January
Katie and I both went to church this morning for the Epiphany service. There was a reasonable congregation but having been so used to celebrating Epiphany with a full choir, I was disappointed, to say the least, that the singing for one of the loveliest Christian festivals of the year should have been so poor.
After the service I decided to make some enquiries to try and track down Angus Spadgwick who had so far proved singularly elusive despite my efforts to contact him using the details provided at the *Dellford Chronicle* offices. I thought my best bet was likely to be the sidesmen and accordingly made a beeline for the pleasant man who'd given me my hymn book as I came in.
"I don't know if you can help me," I said to him, somewhat self-consciously. "I'm looking for this guy who supposedly lives in the village – to be honest I'm not even sure if he exists as he seems completely unobtainable by phone, mobile or email, and having spent all last night trying to get through to him without success I'm beginning to think it's all a big wind-up."
"What's his name?" he enquired.
"Well, that's the ridiculous part," I said, "he rejoices in this extraordinary name. Never heard anything like it before. Sounds made up to me. I'm almost embarrassed to have to say it out loud. Angus Spadgwick!!"
"That would be me," he said, extending his hand. "What can I do for you?"
Conscious that my face had turned the colour of the Mrs Bridges Beetroot Puree that headed our list of unwanted Christmas gifts I gave him sufficient information for him to do a decent little piece in his newspaper column. Following which I decided we should get out as soon as possible.
"Before you go," said Angus, "What did you think of the service?"
"It was nice," I said. "But it would be so good to have a choir even if only occasionally,"
"Oh, there is a choir," he assured me.
"Where?" I enquired, pointing at the empty choir stalls up at the front.

"She'll be back after her hernia operation," he replied. "Till then she's just singing in the congregation. Would have been here today, but she's being taken out to lunch. By her great grandchildren."
"She must be pushing on a bit," I laughed. "One of those poor old dears who keep soldiering on till they literally collapse in the choirstalls. Every choir has one. I guess it's a case of who's got the bottle to tell her it's time to pack it in."
"Yes, probably me," said Angus. "I mean, she should be able to take it from her own son."

Monday 7th January
Katie suggested I place an ad for our inaugural meeting on the 17th in the window of the village shop, so having typed it up I took it to the shop on my way to work this morning and asked the man behind the counter if I could display it.
"Of course," he said. "I'll tell you what, though. It'll look much nicer on one of these coloured cards I've got here." He produced one from under the counter and pressed it into my grateful hand. "There," he said. "That'll be one pound twenty, please."
Having duly parted with that money, I made my way to the front of the shop to place the ad in the window, only to find there was nothing to stick it on with.
"I don't suppose you've got any sellotape, have you?" I asked him.
"No problem," he said with a smile, picking up a packet of sticky tape and offering it to me. "To you, two pounds ninety-five."
Despite the additional inroad into the fiver that had been intended for my lunchtime shopping, I was very pleased with the look of my ad once it had been displayed. My card and adhesive supplier was equally enthusiastic. "Excellent," he said. "You'll be bound to attract loads of singers with that. Do you want me to keep it up there till the night itself?"
I said that would be very kind of him.
"Of course," he said. "Let's see....eleven days, that's – er – twenty-two pounds please."
Spent all day and much of the evening waiting for the flood of calls I trusted would give me a return on my substantial financial outlay, but the blanket of silence was thick enough to insulate the top sixty floors of the Empire State Building.
Which perhaps wasn't surprising, seeing that a late-night examination of the shop window revealed that my ad had been removed. And replaced by one notifying villagers of the availability of a Nearly New Child's Pus Bike.

Friday 11th January

Having decided that a leaflet drop was a better strategy and taken delivery of 200 leaflets from Posters R Us in the Canfield Road Retail Park, I set out on what was a very cold, very windy evening shoving them through letterboxes in the village. When I'd got rid of about forty I found myself at the petrol station at the very top end of the village, and to relieve the tedium of the leaflet-dropping task, I decided to stop for a quick look at Angus Spadgwick's column to see what he'd written about me. Unfortunately I was quite unable to locate it in the news pages. I was just scanning the sports supplement when I heard footsteps approach from behind and a bored female voice asking "Are you going to buy that or ain't yer?"

I turned to see an obese teenage girl whose brown store overalls were complemented somewhat incongruously by green shoes with stiletto heels and who seemed to be on a world mission to promote the wearing of at least three rings on each finger.

"I was just....looking," I said lamely.

"Well, if you want to just look, I suggest you go to the library," she said. "These papers are for selling, not loaning out."

Was so upset by the girl's abrasive manner that, having been effectively bullied into buying the wretched paper, I seemed to lose the impetus to deliver any more leaflets. Instead I walked home, hoping that I had in fact had a sufficiently good plug in Angus' column to arouse the necessary interest. That was, until I located it, not in the second but the fourth supplement, stuck in the middle of the adverts for second-hand cars in the £100 to £250 price range. It was disappointing enough to find my story relegated to such an ignominious place in the paper. But positively maddening to find that Angus saw fit to devote fewer lines to it than the account of how two-and-a-half-year-old Ryan Copplestone had ruined the Christmas festivities at number 3 Pauncefoot Crescent by feeding a Brussels sprout, two roast potatoes, three stuffing balls and a child's portion of gravy to the DVD player.

Sunday 13th January

A late night last night in the Welldiggers Arms, trying in vain to persuade one or two of the locals to come along next Thursday; this after I'd disappointingly been informed that none of the Dippers who'd sung so nicely on New Year's Day live permanently in the village but go away with work for most of the year. I arrived at church for the 10.30 service with Katie rather later than I'd have liked, and with only a few moments to spare to ask the celebrant to mention Thursday's promotional meeting in the week's notices.

As we arrived, I was aware of a number of smartly dressed people standing outside the church smoking cigarettes, and when we entered we saw the church was full with even the side aisles occupied. A glance at the service sheet confirmed that it was a baptism this morning; this was excellent news, as the announcement of Thursday's event would be heard by a far wider audience than I'd expected or dared to hope.
I approached the sidesman, whom I didn't recognise, and asked if it was in order to pop backstage, so to speak, to get a message to the celebrant.
"Sorry, you're too late," the sidesman replied. "He came out and gave the notices a couple of minutes ago. Forgot the banns of marriage, but you can't have everything."
"Oh, one of those priests, is it?" I laughed. "One coupon short of a sandwich toaster?"
"I've always found him very switched on," smiled the sidesman, "as my twin brother."
Fortunately, having banged my head hard against the nearest spare piece of wall, I managed to nab Angus Spadgwick. He promised he would pass my note back to the celebrant without delay and would also ask him to slip the announcement in just after the baptism and the ensuing exchange of the Peace, when the notices were traditionally delivered. Unfortunately, during the Peace I noticed that the celebrant's hands were still extremely full of William Charles who had just been welcomed into the family of Christ's Church. Anxious that my announcement should not go undelivered, I threw a glance at Angus who as a consequence went hurrying up to the celebrant and whispered in his ear.
"Er – yes," the celebrant then said, bringing the Peace to a somewhat abrupt end. "I do have an – ah – extra notice to give at this point." Keeping the baby clasped in his left hand, he reached with his right hand into the pocket of his cassock and pulled out the piece of paper with my notice on it. "On Thurs….." He got no further. Suddenly William Charles, who until then had remained blissfully silent, opened his mouth, uttered a yell and expelled from his inside what looked like the local Mothercare branch's entire month supply of bottled milk, plastering not only his christening outfit but the front of the celebrant's surplice and the celebrant's hitherto pristine copy of *Songs Of Peace And Harmony*. The effect on the celebrant was instantaneous. In panic at the shower of semi-liquid creamy substance that was being heaped ruthlessly upon him, he loosened his grip on my piece of paper which slipped from his hands and fell into the font with a splash. My one last opportunity to promote my new venture drowned in bowl of lukewarm baptismal water. And my chances of a decent turn-out on Thursday instantly reduced to the size of a guide to the subtropical flora and fauna in the puddle on the forecourt of Dellford Automart.

Monday 14th January

Having made repeated visits to the village shop during the week to try and get my card back on display or a refund of £22, and each time found myself speaking to a different assistant who claimed to have no authority to do anything about it, I decided on a bold new strategy this evening. I returned to the shop with a brand new advert plus fresh supplies of sticky tape, waited till I was sure tonight's common-sensically challenged assistant wasn't looking, and walked to the ad display. It wasn't actually attached to the window but to a flimsy wooden board suspended from the wall above by a stout hook, and facing the window. There was no apparent room to place my ad, but a judicious survey of the material on display revealed a shortlist of three for immediate removal: an appeal for the safe return of Sammy the gerbil, posted eighteen months ago; an ad for the WI Old Girls' Coffee Morning which was due to take place a year ago last Tuesday; and an invitation to the Dellford Farmers' Market for "those extra-plump Halloween pumpkins." Thinking that the market organisers might be planning ahead for next Halloween, and not entirely certain of the life expectancy of the domestic gerbil, I gave those two the benefit of the doubt and set about removing the drawing pin holding the WI Old Girls' ad in place. Unfortunately the drawing pin had other ideas, steadfastly refusing to yield and, in a fit of temper, inflicting GBH on my thumb and middle finger. In frustration I placed the card between two uninjured fingers and yanked at it. Immediately there was a hideous crack, the wooden board plus hook plus a quantity of plaster were ripped from the wall, and the board itself came crashing down onto a pile of cardboard boxes of cut-price fruit pies, snapping in half and sending postcards, drawing pins and Tasty Bake apricot tarts slithering across the floor. At the very same moment that last week's purveyor of stationery and advertising space came in through the front door.

"Just send me the bill," I told him. And left.

On return home I got a phone call from Stan Dewsnap, the caretaker at the Assembly Room, to confirm what time to open up for me on Thursday night, and to ask how many chairs I wanted him to put out.

I told him zero was a good figure to aim at. And probably, if anything, on the over-optimistic side.

Thursday 17th January

Arrived at the Assembly Room, through what was advertised on the sign above the main door as the PUB IC ENTRANCE, twenty minutes before the appointed 7.30 starting time. I had absolutely no enthusiasm for what was to come, and was convinced that I would be the only attender. I'd told Katie not to bother to turn up – I didn't want to put her through the humiliation that I was sure would follow, and a particularly crucial stage

had been reached in one of the major *EastEnders* plotlines – so I had no guaranteed punters at all.
The Assembly Room was every bit as gloomy as I'd expected: a dingy, decaying late Victorian building with an unpleasant smell that seemed to mingle Dulux matt emulsion with stale rodent droppings. At least there was hot water, the kettle appeared to function, and there was plenty of sugar, as I discovered when on opening the cupboard labelled SUPPLIES a full bag of Demerara fell out, giving me a nasty bang on the head and knocking my glasses onto the floor.
Stan was very pleasant, however, and having done an emergency repair job on my spectacles was happy to stand and chat with me by the entrance while we waited for the rush of bodies. And at 7.20 we had our first arrival: an extremely rotund man with a very red face and a white shirt which appeared to be struggling to keep itself wrapped around his top half. He introduced himself to me as Charlie and sat down importantly in the front row, breathing heavily through his bulbous red nose and looking impatiently at his watch, as though we were doing him a gross disservice by failing to start early.
"Charlie Tompkins," Stan explained to me in a low voice. "He likes to be involved in absolutely everything that goes on in the Assembly Room. Used to be a magistrate on the Dellford bench, you see."
Having met a number of magistrates in the course of my work, I was interested to hear this. I've always had huge respect for magistrates and felt they do a very difficult and often thankless job. Anybody willing to give so much back to the community, for no reward, had to be worth having on one's side, I thought.
"Has he retired now?" I asked.
"Yes," said Stan. "Came off last year when he hit 70. There was a little court house here in the village, sat at the Assembly Room when they needed the space. Shut down now, of course, health and safety and that malarkey. But he is one formidable guy. Very tough magistrate he was."
"I expect he's got a softer side as well," I said.
"I wouldn't be too sure of that," said Stan. "I can't believe he was allowed to stay on the bench. The way he spoke to people in court. Just before he retired, this poor cow, I've never seen anyone treated the way he treated her. Told her she was a waste of space, a disgusting useless overweight apology for an individual, the last thing he wanted to be doing was spend time listening to her litany of stupidity, and the sooner she went forth and multiplied the better as far as he was concerned. She was shaking like a leaf. It was horrible to watch."
"Well, it may not have done her any harm," I said, "especially if she never came back."
"She had to," said Stan. "She was the clerk of the court."

Presently Angus Spadgwick appeared, followed closely by a dumpy lady with very short and abnormally fat legs. She announced herself as Elphine Mapplebeck. "I'm not much of a singer," she said, "but I'm more than happy to make the tea. You ask for it, and I'll get it for you. Cream teas, scones, cakes, sandwiches, you name it." And she waddled off to sit with Angus behind Charlie in the second row.
I looked gloomily up at the clock to see it was now 7.30 and nobody else had graced us with their presence. And despite my delaying for a further ten minutes, much to Charlie's obvious disgust, there were no further attenders whatever in that time.
Worse was to follow. It soon transpired that of those who were present, none was particularly interested in actually doing any singing. Charlie said he was keen to support a new community initiative in the village and would happily do what was asked of him as long as he was still able to honour his meetings with the Dellford Conservative Association, the Dellford Cricket Club and the Dellford Silly Old Buffers. Angus Spadgwick said he wanted to follow the progress of the new group for his column; Stan said he needed to be around to open and lock up and decided he might as well stay rather than walk the 350 yards back home; and Elphine was already preparing a five-course dinner for the first singers to come through the door. We decided to form a committee and put our joint heads together to see how we were going to achieve what I was setting out to achieve, namely to find some singers. During the next two and a half hours, we talked at great length and reached a momentous decision….to have another meeting.
In the meantime, Charlie's invited me to tea on Sunday when he and his wife will have had time to put together a list of suggested contacts for me to investigate prior to our reconvening in a fortnight.
As the attenders were trooping off and I completed the list of action points from the meeting, consisting of the grand total of no action points at all, I said to Charlie "Well, at least we're in good hands as far as the catering's concerned."
"I wouldn't know," said Charlie. "But if her sister's cooking skills are anything to go by, don't hold your breath. I broke a tooth on the last culinary creation of hers."
"Well, it can happen," I said.
"Not on tomato soup, it can't," said Charlie.
Altogether a great start.

Sunday 20th January
Back to the usual rather geriatric complement at church this morning. When it came to the exchange of the Peace, I turned to the man standing on my left and extended my hand. He simply stood, stock still, giving me

the most perfunctory of grins. I gave up and turned instead to shake hands with a smartly dressed woman behind me, whose comparative youth (about 50) and strong voice made me wonder if she might slot into my group, and saw her give me a knowing and empathetic smile. I'm well aware that not everyone is comfortable with the ritual handshaking which seems so integral to 21st century Eucharistic liturgy, but I still felt a mite foolish at the man's stand-offish reaction. At the end of the service the man sloped off, and as I prepared to leave myself I couldn't resist turning back to the woman, give a glance in the direction he'd taken, and said "Takes all sorts, I guess."

"I suppose so," she replied, "but I dare say you'd have the same difficulty if it was your own arm that had been amputated by a Sainsbury's bacon slicer."

Charlie Tompkins' house was certainly a good deal pleasanter to sit and chat in than the Assembly Room, and the assorted teatime treats provided by his wife were more than acceptable. He produced his list of suggested contacts, which included the church (with perhaps an article in the church magazine), the Internet, the library and the village primary school, pointing out that parents of the children are likely to be on the right side of fifty and some may well relish the opportunity to do something constructive with their leisure time once they've done their offspring's homework for them and *Emmerdale* has finished. However, he seemed less keen to talk about my project than about his work as a magistrate, which I gathered had been the most important aspect of his existence during the past 21 years. He said he could claim to be the principal upholder of justice in Lambsball Green before court business there ceased four years ago, and knew all the old faces inside out.

"Must have been rather difficult to give them a fair trial," I said. "I mean, if you knew them all, wouldn't they just assume you'd find them guilty before the case started?"

Charlie drew in his breath sharply and recoiled, as though I had spoken some dreadful blasphemy. "My dear boy," he said. "In such a case, we trained ourselves to place such matters to the back of our minds and if necessary to announce that we had done so. We listened carefully to the evidence, painstakingly sifting out unreliable or inadmissible material, making judgments on disputed facts and applying the strict criminal standard of proof in assessing whether the facts we'd found amounted in law to a commission of the offence alleged by the Crown." He reached for the tea-strainer. "*Then* we found him guilty."

Although it wasn't practicable to follow many of his leads this evening, I did find time to go on line and do a google search under "Lambsball Green." Only to find myself directed to a schedule of wallpapering options for log cabins in northern Norway and exotic menu additions in the Bushtucker Carvery, Ozzie's Diner, Canberra Road, Tewkesbury.

Wednesday 23rd January

I'd had to get some work done at home over the last couple of nights so hadn't had the chance to look at Charlie's list properly, and had gone to bed last night feeling thoroughly depressed about my new project. Lambsball Green was a large and growing village, but I'd made only a handful of contacts, and Charlie, potentially the most valuable and influential, seemed only interested in himself. I felt no nearer realising my ambition than when I'd started. Leaving aside the village church, where I still felt as out of place as a whale sandwich at a vegan convention in Ashby-de-la-Zouch, there seemed little or no sense of community spirit, no organisations apart from pockets of Neighbourhood Watch, no notion of togetherness….just streets of boxes in which people cocooned themselves between returning from work in the evening and going back to work in the morning.

But as often happens, I felt better after a night's sleep, and turned my attention afresh to the menu of options which Lambsball Green's answer to Judge Jeffreys had provided to me. First up was…..the village church. Charlie had written "Of course, I don't attend that church myself," as though I should have known that even the thought of his dirtying his feet with the dust of St Augustine of Hippo's was repellent to him, but he was gracious enough to suggest some of its members might enjoy forming part of a group of musicians. Yes, I reflected, if I was looking for singers whose blend with each other was no more pure and sensitive than the machinery deployed by Crick's Car Crushing Co-operative in Coldwhistle Road, and who had insufficient confidence in what parts of their body still functioned to be able to remain standing for a piece lasting more than four and a half minutes, let alone sing it in tune. And as for a church magazine, I'd not seen a single copy. The school seemed singularly uninterested: I was told that the secretary was off sick and it was made clear to me that I should wait until she returned before being so inconsiderate as to trouble them again. Which just left the library…..and at last I struck gold. In a file headed "Music and Dramatic Societies" there was a card proclaiming "LOADS – the Lambsball Green Operatic And Dramatic Society. Founded 1921. Director Oswald Pennyfeather M.A. (Oxen). Rehearsals Mondays And Some Tursdays. Contact Tel 5847. More Mumbers Always Welcome."

On the pretext of wanting to be added to the list of mumbers, whatever they might be, I dialled 5847 as directed only to be met by a yawning silence and then a succession of clicks and bleeps which I might have expected had I been trying to connect with the Marks & Spencer "Simply

Food" branch in Beijing, but which seemed somewhat incongruous for a local call to the domicile of O. Pennyfeather Esq. M.A. (Oxen).
Charlie was out tonight when I rang, as were all other members of our fledgling committee, but using the phone directory I checked out the Pennyfeathers that were in there to see if anybody claimed either to be, or to have had any previous dealings with, the erstwhile director of LOADS. Just three Pennyfeathers were listed. None were in Lambsball Green, but there was one in Dellford....who said that he had no musical relations and the only musical performing he'd done had been in a karaoke night at the Red Balloon Club in Ibiza in 1994 but had barely got past the first line of *Tragedy* before the foam cannon was turned on him. The second, living in Greatmere some distance away, said the only relative he had who sang was the famous Crooning Milkman Of Port Talbot – crooning, that was, until an injunction was taken out by homeowners on his round who objected to having "Oh What A Beautiful Morning" belted out at 5am on a wet Monday in November.
Which just left Pennyfeather S.O.B, 'Guys,' Hartley Road, Clendon, a village about twelve miles away, The presence of an O in his initials sowed some modest seeds of optimism, but even those began to shrivel rapidly as I heard the phone answered by an elderly lady.
"Can I speak to Mr Pennyfeather, please?" I began.
"Who?"
"Mr Pennyfeather," I repeated.
"I don't know who you mean," she said. "Can you speak up."
"May I just check I've got this right," I said. "Is that S.O.B. Pennyfeather, 'Guys?'"
"You're a bit late," she said. "Bonfire Night was in November."

Thursday 24th January
Charlie rang me back tonight. He told me he could only spare a moment or two, as he was about to receive a visit from the Dellford Silly Old Buffers, but listened as I told him about my exciting discovery at the library.
"The Lambsball Green Operatic and Dramatic Society," he replied. "is defunct. Folded some years ago. The loss they made having to cancel *Fiddler On The Roof* ended up bankrupting them."
"Why did they have to cancel?" I enquired, thinking that disappointed performers in that show might relish the opportunity to be part of a new musical group.
"It was the male chorus," he replied. "The family, the rest of the villagers, the soldiers and the police. That was the problem."
"What happened to them?" I asked.
"They both dropped dead during the dress rehearsal," said Charlie.

"What about the director, Oswald Pennyfeather?" I wanted to know.
"He was one of them," Charlie replied.
"And do you know anybody who was in that production who might be interested in joining our new group?"
"A few," said Charlie. "But as not a single one of them is now under seventy, I don't suppose you'd have them. Mind you, Georgina Kettlewell is a very useful singer. Still lives in the village. Loves the cinema."
I asked him if he thought it was worth my while to contact her.
"You can if you like," he said, "as long as you feel you can use someone who on her last visit to the Dellford Odeon asked the woman next to her if she was on the right bus to Bury St Edmunds."

Sunday 27th January

Katie suggested we treated ourselves to a lie-in and Sunday brunch. It felt a bit strange not going to church on a Sunday morning, but St Augustine's does a fourth Sunday evensong and I decided to go to that instead, hoping perhaps that the make-up of the congregation might be different and rather more approachable as far as my venture was concerned.
Over our scrambled eggs and bacon, Katie made a good suggestion. At least, it sounded good in the comfort of our kitchen. "Why don't you ask that Angus Spadgwick for copies of some of his village pieces?" she said. "There's bound to be reference there to local community activities and people in the village who've done singing and other sorts of performing. Worth a try, anyway."
I gave Angus a ring and he told me that he's kept copies of every single one of the pieces he's done in the local paper since he started contributing to it over thirty years ago. Accordingly, I've arranged to go and see him on Tuesday night at half past six.
After an invigorating afternoon walk and some tea and cake at home, I went to evensong. Certainly the congregation was different. An average age that was even higher than for the morning service and a total of six people. Plus a priest who rattled his way through the service at a speed indicative either of the need to ensure he kept the undivided attention of the octogenarian shifting uncomfortably in the row in front of me before her bladder forced her to quit the field of play, or the realisation that *Antiques Roadshow* was on half an hour earlier than usual.
On my way out afterwards, I remembered Charlie's church magazine suggestion. I really held out no hope for the existence of the thing and even if it did exist I couldn't see it being of massive help to me. However, as luck would have it I saw the old boy in front of me leafing through a periodical which looked like a church magazine, and I noticed it was

dated next month. Recognising him as a regular member of the congregation, whom I'd seen at most of the services I'd attended at St Augustine's, I hoped he wouldn't object to my approaching him.
"I'm so sorry to trouble you," I said. "Can I have a look at the magazine?"
"Be my guest," he replied, as he handed it to me. I leafed through it. Twenty pages with sixteen pages of adverts, a half-page letter from the vicar, a list of services for February, a children's page with a very feeble wordsearch puzzle and a Bible quiz….just about the most riveting part of the magazine was the revised list of litter collection days for the next six months. I was sure we'd be able to liven it up with articles about our new group and its activities once we'd got going.
I also noticed, and commented to the donor, that there didn't seem to be many references to St Augustine's in the magazine.
"That's because it isn't our church magazine," he said. "We've not had a magazine here at St Augustine's for a few months now. Mind you, they're trying to start it up again, and I've said I'm happy to be appointed as feature writer."
This sounded distinctly promising. I told him I'd be very interested in talking to him again once the appointment had been confirmed, and he in turn said he was confident he could get me, as he put it, "quite a good spread."
After we'd exchanged contact details, I said I ought to be going. "By the way," I said, "if this magazine here isn't ours, whose is it?"
"Colbury, just the other side of Dellford," he replied. "I picked it up this afternoon."
"All I can say is," I said, "I hope our new one turns out better than this. I mean, did you actually have to pay for this apology for a magazine when you picked it up?"
"No, I didn't," he said. "I'm the editor."

Tuesday 29th January

Round to Angus Spadgwick's tonight to look at the back copies of his *Dellford Chronicle* column. Not the most naturally outgoing or effusive type, he seems to lead a somewhat reclusive existence. He told me he'd lost his wife fourteen years ago and now found comfort in his newspaper work. He proceeded to show me the complete collection of his articles going back over thirty years, all kept in meticulous date order. "I used to sign off my column The Spadger," he said conspiratorially. "But I was told that sales of the paper dropped significantly immediately after I started doing it, so I dropped that idea."
Resisting the urge to ask him whether he'd ever actually set foot on Planet Earth, I began turning over the pages. He told me that

"regrettably" he couldn't let me have the originals, but he would use his copier to photograph whichever pieces I wanted. Perhaps predictably there was a mass of completely dry and hopelessly unusable material, although there was a certain surreal humour in the notification of the time of the 2.43pm bus into Dellford being changed, "in response to popular demand," to depart at 2.44pm; the civil action contemplated by one Gerald McKechnie of Castle Crescent, having stepped into an unusually large accumulation of canine deposit, on the ground that the council had negligently failed to repair a sign which apparently prohibited og fuling; and the Monday morning mail delivery which had been delayed after the postman, Clinton Arbuckle, had opened the back door of his home to find his boots stuffed with cold baked beans. True, among the dross there were some vaguely interesting titbits that were conceivably worth following up. But it would be stretching the facts to say that a thrill of anticipatory zeal coursed through my veins at the thought of following up a report on Emma Bagnold's virtuoso performance at the Dellford Civic Hall (of, or on, what it was not revealed), an account of a musical soiree at the home of Maria Agostinelli of Myrtle Road, and lastly an "exclusive in depth" profile of Les Pobsley of Lunar Drive. With a "possibly unequalled talent" for musical farmyard impressions.

Thursday 31st January

The next committee meeting at the Assembly Room. Or rather, it was supposed to be, until Angus and Charlie both rang me with their apologies minutes before I left the house. Stan was there, as was Elphine Mapplebeck who was carrying a large plastic container and proceeded to produce therefrom three handfuls of scones, a pot of cream and a jar of strawberry preserve. But there was really nothing we could meaningfully discuss or carry forward, so instead of a committee meeting we decided to stage the largest cream tea in the history of the universe. Despite the fact that Stan and I had both eaten before we came out, we had no wish to disappoint Elphine, and we dutifully forced down three scones each. The match appeared to be petering out into a high-scoring draw, but in injury time I forced one further scone home, beating Stan at the death. However, my victory was not without its cost: I felt decidedly queasy as Stan took advantage of the lack of committee to show me round the old offices and meeting rooms that had been used when the court had been in session here. We continued through the main waiting area, furnished simply with hard wooden benches, a notice board bearing a single reminder that failure to pay your TV licence could earn you a fine of up to twenty guineas, and three gardening magazines from 1976.

Now feeling the full effects of my unexpected fourth meal of the day, I asked if I could use the toilet, and Stan indicated a door immediately to the right. I wasn't entirely surprised by the state of what I found within. A smell which combined the fragrant essence of rotting kebab with the pungent aroma of Jeyes disinfectant; graffiti adorning every wall; the floor covered in soaked loo paper, lumps of chewing gum and sweet wrappers; and the hot tap producing a jet of ice cold water that bounced so fiercely off the bowl of the sink that my jumper and jeans were drenched within seconds. I made good my escape and rejoined Stan in the foyer.

"Perhaps if I may I can use the magistrates' toilet next time," I requested.

"That was the magistrates' toilet," he replied.

A superb first month. Singers – zero. Committee members – five on a good day with the wind behind. And venue – probably about as much charisma and potential appeal to the budding Katherine Jenkins or Russell Watson as the revenue protection officers' smoking room in Cowdenbeath bus station.

FEBRUARY

Sunday 3rd February

At last this morning at church, I thought I'd make a breakthrough. While we were receiving communion a man came up from the back of the church and sang a quite beautiful solo version of Franck's *Panis Angelicus*. He wasn't a young man, by any means – I guess he was in his late fifties – but his voice had a remarkable purity for one so comparatively advanced in years.

Afterwards I went up, introduced myself, and congratulated him. Thanking me profusely, he told me his name was Alan Broadhurst and he was now living in Lambsball Green once more after a lengthy absence. He explained that he'd been living and working away from this area for the last four years, but he'd got back on Friday and hopefully would not have to go away again for a couple of years at least. He also introduced me to his wife Debbie, who has resumed her previous post as church organist.

I told him about my new venture and gave him my contact details, and he sounded extremely interested. He told me he'd been the only tenor in the church choir for several years and did quite a lot of solo work, not only locally but in London and abroad.

"So tell me," he said, "where are your new group meeting?"

"Nowhere, yet," I said. "We've only got as far as forming a committee which is meeting at the Assembly Room at the moment."

"I suppose there's really nowhere else," said Alan, with a sympathetic smile.

"No," I said. "It really is the most godforsaken dump. Embarrassing to have to ask people to leave their firesides to come along and spend more than five precious minutes of their lives there. Goodness knows who designed the wretched thing."

"My great grandfather," said Alan. "Excuse me. Busy morning."

It turned into a wet miserable afternoon. Katie was having to work so I found myself on my own and at a loose end, feeling more negative and pessimistic about my venture than at any time since I'd started. Decided, on impulse, to borrow the Assembly Room key from Stan and begin a clean-up of the place, starting with that awful magistrates' washroom. Although I got the rubbish cleared up quickly enough, I was less successful with the graffiti, and a good hour's completely unproductive scrubbing and half a bottle of Muscle Man Wall Stain Cleanser (*Tested On Toughest Surfaces – Guaranteed Worst Graffiti Removed Or Your Money Back*) later and with a decent football match on TV to go home to, I was still being informed that ROBBO RULES OK but with tantalisingly no information as to Robbo's identity or credentials. Then again, with the very future of my project hanging in the balance, I've more important things over which to lose sleep than wondering whether Robbo is an affectionate nickname for the district Presiding Judge or the local vagrant who's been keeping the court house in business by notching up a century in convictions for being drunk and incapable.

Tuesday 5th February

After a number of unsuccessful attempts to get hold of the Lambsball Green Primary School, I finally tracked the secretary down first thing and asked if I could pop round during the lunch period one day soon to see her and discuss publicising my new venture through the school. She spoke to me as though I were one of her annoying children. "Come today if you want," she said. "But make sure you're here between one fifteen and one forty-five, and not a moment after."

Typically I got caught in a meeting which didn't finish till one twenty, and with every set of traffic lights against me, I struggled to make it from my office to the school by bike in the 20 minutes available. The school was a pleasant modern building with extensive fields and ample sporting opportunities, of which I got a taste when I was struck in the face by a ball which a number of children in PE gear were endeavouring to propel towards what was conspicuously signed as the Hubert Babbage Memorial Basketball Net. Despite it being quite a cold day, sweat was pouring off me as I hurried through the main door and headed for the clearly-signed school office. When I got there I saw a tall, thin, matron-like woman with severe thick glasses and even more severely swept-back hair glowering over a sullen-looking boy with sticking-out earlobes of which one was noticeably larger than another and a haircut that was closer than the atmosphere in the Amazon rainforest immediately before a summer thunderstorm.

"Connor," she barked, "That's the third time this morning that I've told you not to come into my office without permission. If it happens again, you're for it. Is that clear?"

The boy nodded.

"Now just get out of my sight," she said.

He slunk off, leaving me alone with Matron, whose icy glance at the retreating juvenile positively defied anybody, not just recidivist year two pupils, to approach within a hundred yards of her without police escort and bullet-proof vest. Her glacial features thawed only marginally as she turned to me, introduced herself to me as the secretary, and enquired how she could help me. I explained to her the purpose of my visit, namely to ask if my new venture might be publicised among the parents of children at the school. I produced a written note, in the form of a press release,

with all the relevant details and asked if it might be reproduced in the school newsletter.
"February one's already out," she snapped. "So you're too late for that."
"It could wait till next month," I said.
"That'll be March," she said with relentless logic. "There's always a lot of important material that needs to go into the March newsletter. Very busy month here. I could probably only squeeze in a few lines at the end of page six under Miscellaneous. Most parents tend not to get as far as page six anyway."
"I see," I said, feeling like a rabid poodle being fed crumbs from a banqueting table.
"I'll tell you what might be a better bet," she went on. "The Parent Teacher Association. They organise quite a few events for parents and are always interested in new ideas. I'll give you the PTA secretary's details."
She went to her desk and opened a file full of papers, but after a few minutes' rifling through it she was quite unable to locate what she wanted. "It must be in the Head's office upstairs," she said angrily, as though I were responsible for moving it there in the first place. "If you give me a few minutes I'll go and fetch it."
Once she'd left, my attention was drawn to a trolley close to the door on which were a mixture of clean and dirty cups, an urn that when I felt it was still hot, and a tupperware container labelled COFFEE. Obviously there had just been a meeting and these had been the refreshments. I was desperate for a drink after some four hours with not a jot of caffeine and then a thirst-inducing bike ride, and having heard Matron clomp her way slowly up the stairs I reckoned I just had time to grab a quick cuppa before she began the equally unsteady and equally audible descent. I poured some hot water into one of the clean cups then grabbed the container and pulled hard at the lid. Rather too hard, as it turned out. The effect was dramatic. As the lid came away, there was suddenly a veritable explosion of coffee beans and the entire contents of the container were spewed all over the top surface of the trolley and the surrounding floor area. I gave myself a moment to survey the scene of devastation, then as I heard fresh clompings on the stairs, I did what any calm, self-possessed and rational professional person would have done. I made a dash for it.
As I headed for the exit door I heard an almost hysterical scream of "CONNOR!" but I didn't dare stay to see what hideous punishment might befall the wretched boy who was now bearing the weight of my sins. But I guessed that he'd be lucky to escape simply with a week's cessation of tuck rations. And far more likely to be found, for the next few hours at least, suspended by the larger of his two earlobes from the Hubert Babbage Memorial Basketball Net.

Thursday 7th February

Things are looking up at last.

To my amazement, I got a phone call from Alan Broadhurst today. He told me that he was well aware that the Assembly Room was in dire need not only of the clean I'd attempted to make a start on on Sunday, but complete refurbishment and redecoration; apart from the church and the pub, it was the only community facility in the village and yet it wasn't used regularly by any groups or societies. He suggested that to prevent his great grandfather's glorious legacy from becoming even more of a laughing stock than it obviously was, we formed a working party to do something about it. We agreed to meet for a drink in the Welldiggers tonight.

In the pub, over a very welcome pint of beer, Alan told me that subject to work and other singing commitments he'd be delighted to be part not only of my new group but also the Assembly Room clean-up working party and suggested we met with Stan next week to discuss the practicalities. When I told him that we had a committee meeting next Thursday, we agreed it would be best if we all met together and perhaps postpone to the Friday to avoid Valentine's night.

I told him about the progress I'd made so far, and the acquaintances I'd made: Elphine Mapplebeck, the Fanny Craddock of Lambsball Green, Angus Spadgwick, the most boring columnist still living, the Lambsball Green Dippers, and Charlie the caustic and egotistical hanging judge. I was only too aware that the list was pitifully short. "I mean, there's no community life as such in this village at all," I said. "Not even a parish council, it seems."

"Oh, there's a parish council," said Alan. "Used to meet at the Assembly Room until they realised they all lived in Dellford so they started meeting there instead."

"Would they support my new group?" I asked him.

"Probably the reverse," said Alan, "if the experience of Rodney Statham is anything to go by. He was probably the last person before you who had an idea of organising a community event in the village and for the village and who was foolish enough to approach the council for their support and approval. Before he could proceed they insisted on a full Health & Safety risk assessment, the taking up of references from his present and past employers, a full Criminal Records Bureau check, a certificate from Social Services confirming they had no child protection concerns about him and he was a fit and proper person to work with children, and the grant of a public entertainment licence under the Local Government (Miscellaneous Provisions) Act 1976."

"What was his event?" I asked.

"Sponsored pink grapefruit juggling in the church car park," said Alan.

Sunday 10th February

To church alone for the first Sunday in Lent. I got there slightly late and found myself sitting next to two women, an elderly one and, immediately next to me, a much younger one, I guessed in her early to mid-thirties, with very short hair and dressed in a baggy sweat shirt, jeans and trainers. I was sitting nearest the aisle and out of politeness when the time came to receive communion, I stood aside to allow them to go up first, but the younger one stood still and gave me one of the filthiest looks I think I had ever suffered. Immediately after the service she said she would like to have a "quiet word" with me. Feeling like an errant schoolboy caught with bicycle oil on his best trousers, I joined her in a side aisle.

"I just thought I ought to say I was quite offended by your actions during the communion," she said. "First, as far as I am concerned, women and men are equal and women don't appreciate being patronised by meaningless gestures, however well intended. Secondly, I felt you were placing me under wholly improper pressure to participate in the rituals of a certain belief system which it cannot be presumed I am prepared to accept."

I was mortified. Especially as I had been so anxious not to commit any further acts of alienation of fellow members of the church of St Augustine of Hippo. "I am so sorry," I said to her. "I suppose I assumed, that's all."

"Well, let's just draw a line under it," she said, and made to leave.

Anxious to avoid leaving the church feeling the size of a pepper pot at a stick insects' luncheon party, I thought the least I could do was introduce myself and ask her for her name.

"It's Flora," she replied, in a slightly mellower tone. "Flora Sandstrom. My first name was constantly mocked by bullies throughout my schooling. You know, margarine jokes, all the rest of it, and looking back on it I see how deeply offensive it all was. Nobody can help the name they were given."

I thought it might be tactful to change the subject and told her about my new venture, even being so bold as to ask her if she might be interested.

"I used to enjoy choral singing," she replied, "till I found it impossible to reconcile the largely sectarian content of the words with my own humanist philosophy. I'm just about to start a humanist society in the village in fact, endeavouring to attract those who accept the validity of the belief system of each person of all faiths and none and who are as offended as I am by those, particularly in the popular press, who label basic respect for fellow beings as political correctness. You're welcome to come along if you wish. Assembly Room. First meeting Monday week, half past seven."

With her mention of the Assembly Room I realised that although our standpoints on life were as far apart as those of Genghis Khan and Mr

Blobby, we might actually find we had a common purpose. Moments later, she was saying she'd be delighted to consider co-operating with the clean-up working party I was setting up with Alan and would also promote my musical venture among her own membership which she was confident could be significant. Suddenly, we were the best of friends.
Elated that a social encounter which had started so disastrously was ending so promisingly, I walked with her down towards the exit. On the way, I chanced to see Alan nearby. "Alan," I said confidently, indicating my new friend beside me. "I'd like you to meet a new working-party member for the Assembly Room. Flora Sandstorm."

Wednesday 13th February

Rang Stan to confirm all was well for Friday night's meeting.
"Fine," he said. "I've got some really good news. The council, who own the building, have agreed to finance redecoration of the place. Complete refurbishment. I've got the decorators lined up to come in and make a start next week and I've even managed to get Edna Mudge to join us on Friday."
"Who's she?" I asked.
"The Assembly Room cleaner," he said. "Lovely lady. So they say."
I asked if he was prepared to elaborate on that.
"Well," said Stan, "not even Charlie in his most vindictive mood managed to force me to hide in the broom cupboard for an entire court session. Mind you," he went on hastily, "she has her uses."
"In what way?" I enquired.
"One evening they couldn't use Dellford court house for some reason and they had to move some very lengthy and even more pointless meeting here," he said. "Five o'clock kick-off, twenty-seven items on the agenda. By six fifty, they'd just completed item 1, apologies, and item 2, agree minutes of the last meeting. By half past seven, they were out. Agenda complete."
"How's that?" I asked.
"I told them that at quarter to eight prompt, Edna Mudge would be arriving with a vat of super-concentrate bleach and a spray gun," said Stan, "and wouldn't be afraid to use them."

Friday 15th February

Arrived at the Assembly Room in good time for our meeting, but had barely said hello to Stan than a minor explosion heralded the arrival of a female I had never seen before but who was obviously Edna Mudge. She was a surprisingly diminutive woman in her late forties with a shock of untidy dark hair and dressed in a blue gingham coat. "I want a word with

you, Dewsnap," she said, slamming a book down on the table. "Just what do you think you're playing at?"
"Come again, Edna?" enquired Stan feebly, cowering into the deeper recesses of his upright wooden chair.
"Look at this," she said. "I've just found out you've booked a decorator in for next Wednesday."
"Er – yes, if you say so," Stan stuttered.
"Without checking my diary," Edna barked, pointing at the book she had just placed on the table. "Look at this, will you. Entry for 20th February. Next Wednesday, in case the fact had escaped your notice."
Stan strained his eyes to read it. "High Sheriff beds Ted?" he queried. "He's kept that very quiet."
"Don't be stupid," Edna snapped, picking up the diary and waving it accusingly in Stan's face. "The High Sheriff is meeting Mr Tompkins here that day. And in honour of his visit, I've arranged that morning to have the old bedstead collected from the back yard along with all the other junk that's out there. This isn't a community hall, it's a tip. Could do with a damn good clean, if you ask me."
At that moment Charlie Tompkins strode in, sweat on his forehead and breathing heavily, followed closely by Flora Sandstrom, attired in an oversized woolly jumper and skirt, and faded white gym shoes. "Let me introduce you," I said to Charlie, determined to get her name absolutely right this time. "Charlie, this is Flora. Flora Sandstrom."
Charlie gave her a fierce handshake. "Welcome, dear lady," he said, garlic very evident on his heavy breath. "Live in the village, do you?"
"I do, yes," said Flora.
"Married?"
"I'm not, no," said Flora.
"Never mind," Charlie observed. "Can I make a suggestion? If you want to get yourself a fella, try a new wardrobe. With a nice blouse and skirt that fit you, for a start."
Mercifully, Alan arrived at that moment, with Elphine just a little way behind him, and Angus Spadgwick bringing up the rear. Elphine opened a picnic basket and produced a cylindrical carton of crisps, a selection of sandwiches and three cocktail sticks attached to which were flags labelled HAM, TURKEY and SAMMON PAIST. Evidently spelling wasn't something that came to Elphine as naturally as cooking.
We got going on our meeting soon afterwards. Discussion was unfortunately hampered by a number of things. Elphine's sandwiches, while tasty, were somewhat indigestible and after a couple of rounds each, everyone was beginning to regret their decision to eat before they came out, not least Charlie, whose pre-meeting chicken curry was, to employ his delicate phraseology, "all ready to make a reappearance." He

hardly endeared himself to Flora by persisting in calling her Fiona and, on being informed she was a vegetarian, apologising for the absence of sandwiches with nut cutlet fillings. Flora restricted her comments to muttering that "if that oaf makes one more offensive remark I'm out of here" but otherwise sat back in her chair reading an obviously well-thumbed copy of *The Portable Humanist*. Angus Spadgwick sat there in a cocoon of silence that reminded me of the time I stepped into a train at Hampton Wick and found myself sitting in a no-mobile-phone-or-personal-stereo carriage next to a nun with laryngitis. And Edna Mudge sat chewing gum very audibly, reminding us at regular intervals of the impossibility of starting redecoration work until the High Sheriff was safely off the premises.

After an hour and a half of discussion, we agreed that to pacify Edna Mudge we would postpone the decorators till the week after next; on Saturday 29th March, the work complete, we will spend the day tarting the place up; then that same evening we'll have a grand reopening followed by a buffet supper at the Assembly Room, open to everyone, with Alan providing some musical entertainment. Alan kindly said he'd oversee the practical arrangements for the day while I agreed to deal with the publicity side. It will be a proper community event. Flora can recruit some humanists, I can recruit some singers, and maybe others in the village can promote their own particular activities. It all sounds ideal. But I'm deeply conscious that word of mouth agreement is a far cry from actually getting on with it. Notwithstanding that Elphine has already promised us a choice of seventeen different types of cherry tomato for the salad table.

At five past nine I declared the meeting closed. Angus placed three of the remaining 43 sandwiches in his Sainsbury's carrier bag. Elphine said next time she'd bring something "rather easier on the stomach" – to wit, her chocolate bread and butter pudding. And Edna Mudge spat out her chewing gum, scoring an impressive direct hit on the waste-paper basket a full 15 yards away.

"Isn't it customary to end these meetings in prayer?" Charlie Tompkins enquired, looking mischievously in Flora's direction.

Flora slammed her *Portable Humanist* shut. "What?" she demanded.

"I'm so sorry, Fiona," he said. "It never occurred to me that suggestion would upset you."

Flora finally snapped. "My name's Flora, not Fiona," she said. "Are you deliberately trying to offend me?"

"Certainly not," grinned Charlie, as he forced his body, now the larger by eight turkey, one ham and two sammon paist doorsteps, from his seat. "But no doubt I'd manage it if I tried."

And Flora, plus her *Portable Humanist*, stormed out.

Frankly I think the High Sheriff's bedroom activities are the least of our worries.

Sunday 17th February

A late night last night, enjoying a meal with Katie and friends from work, so decided not to go to church this morning. Thus creating, I hoped, a gaffe-free day of rest for once.

Had just finished reading the football reports in the paper when Alan phoned. "Missed you at church this morning," he said. "You'd obviously forgotten."

"Forgotten what?" I asked.

"That you were supposed to be reading the first lesson," he replied. "Len Huckleby volunteered to do it instead."

I groaned inwardly. "I'm so sorry," I said. "I'm sure he did a better job than I would have done."

"Never got the chance," said Alan. "On his way up to read, he tripped up and fell flat on his face."

"Was he very badly hurt?" I asked.

"There were no bones broken," Alan assured me. "And the emergency dentist said his front teeth must have been due for extraction anyway."

He went on to tell me the other reason for his call was to advise that next weekend he and a couple of friends were meeting up to do a major clearance job on the back yard of the Assembly Room as part of the refurbishment operation, and would Katie and I like to join them to help and then have a pub lunch with them afterwards.

"I thought Edna Mudge was clearing that out this week," I said.

"Oh, she'll shift the heavy stuff," said Alan. "Or rather, tell Stan to do it, and Stan being Stan and wanting to keep his private parts attached to the rest of him, he'll do it. But there's loads of stuff there they'll never get to. And it's not all junk. Needs sorting through anyway."

"I might pop down later and check it out myself," I said.

"I wouldn't, if I were you," said Alan. "Edna and one of her sidekicks have this idea that kids use it for drug dealing. They're often round there, hoping to catch someone in the act. If you want to go, wait till Thursday afternoon when she's out bowling. She caught two men in there once, gave them hell, got the police round, everything. We certainly never saw them again round these parts."

"And did they find any drugs?" I asked.

"I don't think so," said Alan, "seeing the two men were the chief executive of the county council and the chairman of the local Crime and Disorder Reduction Partnership."

Monday 18th February

An excellent day at work which included our booking, at very short notice, ten days' holiday starting at the end of the month. But certainly the afternoon was overshadowed by the prospect of Flora's Humanist Society inaugural meeting, which I'd promised her I'd attend, and which was due to start at six thirty.

"Back at eight, no later," said Katie. "That's when dinner's on the table. Your favourite."

"No problem," I assured her. "Hopefully I'll be back within the hour."

Arrived at the Assembly Room just before half past six, to find Flora there and just two others: a middle-aged greasy-haired man in a Barbour jacket and brown corduroy trousers, and a rather older white-haired woman whose garb was altogether trendier, sporting faded jeans and bright yellow shoes with Doc Marten soles. All three of them stood round a television that had been placed on a table in the middle of the room.

"Excellent," I said in jocular tones. "So we won't miss *EastEnders* after all."

To judge by their reaction to my remark one would have thought I had suggested an evening belly dancing in the municipal cemetery.

I took the opportunity before the meeting started to ask them if they lived in the village and whether they sang. The man said he could give a passable rendition of *Knees Up Mother Brown* in the bath but lived twenty-eight miles away, and the woman said that although she lived on the edge of the village she was, as she stated somewhat cryptically, "tone deaf and proud of it."

At that moment Flora said we may as well be starting, and called the meeting to order. "Welcome," she said to the three of us. "Sorry about the coffee but the urn seems to have broken. Without further ado I'll hand over to Joss Fairbrother who's leading our meeting tonight. His subject is denial of human rights by religious governments." I felt like asking what about the denial of the human right to a caffeine injection before a meeting, but bit it back. And with that, the Barbour-jacketed man came forward and began to speak.

During the first 30 minutes of Joss' talk, devoted almost exclusively to his early years and his Damascus-road conversion to non-belief, I kept half an eye on the door, hoping against hope that somebody might have the decency to join the gathering and tell me they were a villager with a great singing voice. But no such being materialised and in the next 30 minutes of his talk, a damning indictment of the evils committed by man in the name of religion, I began to think about legitimate and face-saving ways of making my escape, all too well aware of Flora's endurance of the whole of last Friday's meeting, Charlie Tompkins' jibes notwithstanding. However, no good ideas came to mind, and I resigned myself to

continuing to have to listen to Joss as he proceeded to announce his intention to show us some DVD footage of torture practised by supposedly God-fearing states. "I warn you," he said, "you'll find the content extremely disturbing."
And I'm sure we would have done. Had, that is, any of us known how to work the DVD. For the next 40 minutes we each had a go at pressing every button on the remote control until we'd tried out every conceivable sequence, only to be rewarded for most of those sequences with a screen as empty as a guide to British Home Stores coffee shops in Zanzibar. When something did come up on the screen it was to advise us to REFER TO HELP MENU, or that ominously there was a SYSTEM ERROR, more ominously an ADVANCED SYSTEM ERROR, more ominously still a SERIOUS SYSTEM ERROR, even more ominously a SEVERE SYSTEM ERROR and most ominously of all, a direction to CONTACT SUPPLIER. At last, however, a picture emerged, which did indeed seem to show a hapless-looking man sitting in a chair while another stood over him with an instrument and talking very excitedly in a wholly unintelligible foreign language, but so fuzzy was the picture that it was impossible to tell whether this was the Iranian secret police extracting a confession in an underground cell in one of the dingier suburbs of Tehran or an advertisement for a Saudi Arabian brand of hair clippers.
Finally at twenty past eight, when this scene was replaced by another blank screen and an entreaty to SEND ERROR REPORT IMMEDIATELY, I told the assembled group that I had an urgent appointment and needed to go.
"So clearly you don't regard the humiliating treatment experienced by Youssuf Rehal as important as your warm comfortable home, free from the fear of being dragged from your bed at three in the morning, interrogated ruthlessly and ceaselessly for sixteen hours and denied access to basic human hygiene, legal representation and even a telephone to inform family and loved ones of your internment, all in the name of a supposedly loving God," said Flora accusingly.
Not with the spectre hanging over me of my packed overnight bag on the doorstep together with one saucepanful of congealed boeuf Bourgignon and another of cold mashed potato.

Thursday 21st February
Was enjoying an uneventful and relatively stress-free day at work when suddenly at three thirty, without warning, all the lights went off and the computers went dead. A call to the local electricity company confirmed there was a major power failure affecting the centre of Dellford and supplies were unlikely to be restored for three hours. The boss said we might as well all leave early.

Remembering that Thursday was Edna Mudge's bowling afternoon, I decided to go and take a look at the Aladdin's cave in the back yard of the Assembly Room. I'd never explored the back yard, but a quick look at what there was confirmed Alan's suspicions. Obviously despite what may have been cleared by Edna or rather by Stan yesterday, there was still a huge amount of rubbish there, but contrary to what Alan implied there really was nothing worth salvaging at all and the sooner it was carted off to the tip the better.

I bent down to examine a heap of old newspapers, on which was perched an enormous green large-wheeled recycling bin half on its side, when suddenly I heard the unmistakable sound of Edna Mudge. "Maxine! Doreen! There's someone round the back!" she yelled with a voice that could grate a frozen catering-size portion of Red Leicester.

"Keep your voices down!" Another woman's voice with a texture and purity of rainwashed gravel. "You go and call the police, Doreen. Edna and I will trap them and keep them talking till they get here."

"Drug-crazed psychopathic brain-dead imbeciles," I heard a third voice pronounce. "I hope they lock em up and throw away the key." And when this even more formidable-sounding female added "Go in and get them" I decided that, although theirs was hardly the most sophisticated form of covert surveillance I had experienced, discretion was the better part of valour. I lifted the flap of the wheelie bin, which thankfully was empty, and crawled inside.

For the next few minutes my heart was thumping and I began to feel like one of the persecuted fugitives of whom Joss had spoken with such eloquence and at such length on Monday. The two women, whose bowling I learned had been curtailed by the same power cut, kept prowling round and round the yard, and each time one of them came up to the bin I was convinced I was going to be discovered. They were soon joined by the third who I heard report that the police weren't interested, prompting Edna to suggest her own, far nastier-sounding, form of summary justice. But after what seemed like an eternity of investigative footsteps, I heard Gravel Voice say "No good. They must have got out through the bushes. Let's go home."

I decided to wait a few minutes until the footsteps had receded completely. But even as I was preparing cautiously to open the flap and eject, I heard more footsteps approaching and more voices. These of a much more juvenile variety. "Shall we race them down Pullen's Passage?" I heard one say.

"Yeah, why not," came another voice.

And suddenly I felt a jerk – a right jerk, truth to tell – and found myself on the move.

I tried to shout, but my cries were in vain, drowned out by the shrill shrieks of a select handful of Lambsball Green's youth indulging in the simple unsophisticated joys of wheelie-bin racing. For a brief second after this period of taxi-ing the bin came to rest, giving me a fleeting chance of escape, but before I could lift the flap I felt a sharp push and heard a loud cheer. Suddenly I was off again in a different direction, this time heading downhill and inexorably gaining speed, with the deafening roar of the wheels on tarmac getting louder and louder as the gradient of Pullen's Passage, which I knew to be the steepest hill in the village, intensified. I couldn't recall what lay at the bottom, but it didn't take long to find out. There was a sudden bump as the bin crashed down onto its side with a loud thud, and came to rest.
Very cautiously, I opened the flap and crawled out. Immediately my senses were assailed by the most appallingly pungent stench, and as my pupils adjusted to the fading afternoon light, I found myself lying on top of what would have to be one of the principal contenders for Lambsball Green's Compost Heap Of The Year award. Five minutes later I was trudging up Pullen's Passage with fragments of over-ripe banana still dripping from my shirt front and fragments of carrot peelings attached to my left earlobe, exuding an aroma which would have got me excluded from the Dellford Chips And Cholesterol With Everything Café on health and safety grounds. Reflecting that perhaps after all I should have taken my chances with Edna Mudge and her rubber sink plunger.

Sunday 24th February
A good session with Alan yesterday was followed by a frankly uninspiring service this morning. Indeed the highlight was the announcement by the celebrant that "after months of closure for repairs, the toilets are once again functioning, with brand new flush mechanism. In case you've forgotten where the toilets are, go up into the north aisle, look for the silver symbols and the arrow on the white door and – ah – keep walking!"
By coincidence I was once again seated next to a younger woman I'd not met before. Determined not to allow Flora's verbal onslaught of two weeks ago to deter me from sticking to basic rules of etiquette, I stood aside to enable her to go up to receive communion and she accepted gratefully. She was, I guessed, in her late twenties or early thirties and had attractive brown hair and a lovely smile. Afterwards she told me her name was Amanda, and she was renting a house in the village. I asked her if she sang, and she said she was doing an Open University music degree and actually looking for a choir to join. I could hardly believe my good fortune.

I asked her if she could give me a contact number. "I will if you give me one sec," she said. "I must just go and use the felicities."
Perhaps because of the number of references to water during the service, from the hymn to "those in peril on the sea" and the psalm asking our Lord to "wash me thoroughly from my sins," I decided I could do with using the gents' felicities myself, so I followed Amanda to the white door in the north aisle as directed. I let her open the door so we could keep walking as instructed by the celebrant – only to find myself following her into a single room consisting of one WC and wash basin.
Amanda turned to me in a mixture of horror and bewilderment. "What the hell do you think you're doing?" she demanded.
With cheeks as red as a strawberry-juice-stained gas bill reminder, I slammed the door shut and walked away as rapidly as I dared. Another promising lead blown to smithereens.
"Well," said Katie when I told her what had happened, "I don't know why they spent so much money on a new flush mechanism. Because for letting things go down the toilet you are in a class by yourself."

MARCH

Monday 10th March

Back from holiday, and down to work in earnest. Hoping to discover some as yet untapped musical talent in the village, I'd used some of my time away to obtain details of three music societies in Dellford. I spoke first to the secretary of the Dellford Choral Society who told me she couldn't give details of any of the membership as it was contrary to the Data Protection Act, but why didn't I come to their first rehearsal back after the Easter break in April, half of which would take the form of a social evening. The secretary of the Dellford Amateur Operatic, one Margaret Donaldson, told me she couldn't give details of any of the membership as it was contrary to the Dating Prevention Act but I'd be welcome to come along when they started their rehearsals for *The Mikado*. In May. And when I tried the number of the secretary of the Dellford Happy Harmonists, the man who answered told me his sister was the one with all the information but I'd need to call her as she wasn't in. "When's the best time to call?" I enquired. "In five weeks," he replied, "by which time she should be back from New Zealand."

And so I found myself forced back to the list of doubtful celebrities I'd extracted from Angus' *Chronicle* column back at the end of January, which I'd put in the compartment of my filing cabinet labelled ABSOLUTE LAST RESORT. First on the list was Emma Bagnold of Cloud Close, who four years ago had given her virtuoso performance in Dellford's Civic Hall. Her husband told me yes, it had been a most successful evening of popular song, yes, she was still living in the village, and yes, she still had a great voice and loved anything to do with performing. I was getting quite excited. "And I'm sure she'd have loved to join you," he went on, "were it not for the fact that she's already late."

"What for?" I asked.

"The triplets should have arrived three days ago," he replied.

Next it was Maria Agostinelli who eighteen months ago had thrilled her audience with a musical soiree of grand opera in her home in Myrtle Road – but who was now, I found, thrilling audiences with musical soirees of grand opera in her new home in Number 6A Via Giacomo Papadelle, Brindisi.

Which just left Les Pobsley of Lunar Drive whose wife, when I rang his number, told me what his peculiar talent was and assured me he'd call back as soon as he returned from the pub.

So here I am. Delaying my bedtime awaiting a call from someone whose musical credentials consist of singing Elgar's *Pomp & Circumstance March* in the style of Donald Duck.

Thursday 13th March
With no call from Donald Duck on or since Monday, was still no further forward. During an idle five minutes at work, decided to do one other bit of PR for the gala opening, namely attempt to get a slot on our local commercial radio station, Love It FM. I wasn't hugely optimistic but within ten minutes of contacting them using the email address on the website, I got an email back asking me to call Becky. I duly did so and gave her all the details.
"To be honest, we're a bit tight on space for the next few weeks," she said. "I suppose I could get you a half hour slot on Mark Adam's show. He's on Tuesdays to Saturdays, one thirty to five thirty. Let's see – Tuesday 25th from 3.15 to 3.45 looks good. To be there by 3 to get set up. You're familiar with Mark Adam and his programme?"
"Oh yes," I said. In the circumstances I could hardly admit I didn't know Mr Adam from....well, Adam. "So, I can really have a full half hour to talk about the project? Less obviously interruptions for news and travel?"
"No, you should be uninterrupted," said Becky.
"And if there are any big important news stories that squeeze me out you'll let me know and cancel me in good time?" I asked, recalling I'd been caught that way once before on local radio. I didn't want to take an afternoon off work and endure an 80-mile round trip to sit silently in a windowless booth for two hours with nothing for company save a carton of tepid vending machine hot chocolate. And then be told I'd been cut out.
"I can't see that's at all likely," said Becky.
I could hardly believe my good fortune. "That's brilliant," I said. "I'd love to do it."
"Okay," said Becky. "So that's Tuesday 25th March at our studios in Redford Road. I'll send you instructions as to how to get into the building."
"Won't there be anyone on the reception desk?" I queried.
"No, I'm afraid not," said Becky. "Not at 3.15 in the morning."

Palm Sunday 16th March
A good congregation for Palm Sunday, with more communicants than I'd seen for a long time. It seemed an excellent opportunity to mention the Assembly Room opening on the 29th and I made a point of approaching the surprisingly youthful-looking celebrant beforehand and asking if he could be sure to mention it in the notices. "Of course," he said. "I'll be doing them just before the final blessing. Having said that, I'm bound to forget, and if I do, I'm quite happy for you just to yell it out from the congregation."

The large number of attenders seemed to catch the stewards off guard, and when the time came for the congregation to take communion they didn't do the best job of marshalling everybody up to the altar rail. Consequently there was quite a wait in the aisle and after I had finally received, I found myself, having waited behind three rather portly old ladies, unaccountably returning from the altar in front of them and making my way down to several rows of empty pews, quite unable to recall which was mine. Remembering that I had dropped my palm cross and seeing one lying on the floor, I retrieved it and sat down nearby. At that moment, a severe-looking woman with several chins, very tight-fitting floral dress and stockings that failed to conceal her varicose veins marched into the pew and proceeded to sit down beside me. In fact, to say she sat beside me wasn't quite accurate, as her left buttock descended heavily to make unwelcome contact with the outside of my trouser pocket and place scarcely tolerable pressure upon what lay therein. Resisting the temptation to remind her that the words "Excuse me" were still very much part of the English language, I shifted to my left, bringing my own rather less ample but equally firm posterior down with a large crunch onto a pair of carelessly-placed spectacles. Seconds later, the owner of the aforementioned optical aid, who only a few minutes previously had publicly offered prayers to the Almighty for a new spirit of unselfishness, inclusiveness, tolerance and understanding amongst the brotherhood of nations and Christian communities arrived on the scene and was demanding to know who had given me the right to occupy a pew that was reserved to her on the third and fifth Sunday of every alternate month on which there was no celebration at eight in the morning save the ninth and twenty-first Sundays after Trinity, where I expected her to find the three hundred and forty-six pounds eighty-seven pennies plus value added tax that it would cost her to replace her newly fitted and purchased frames when her optician opened for business on Monday morning, and how I thought with her failing eyesight she could possibly proceed with her planned motor journey to visit her son and daughter-in-law in Gussage St Michael.

After which the failure of either the celebrant or myself to remember to announce the reopening of the Assembly Room was a matter of the most trifling importance.

Tuesday 18th March

A reassuring phone call from Alan telling me that all the practical arrangements were in hand for the 29th and all that was needed now was support from the village for the evening function.

I also got a phone call, amazingly, from someone responding to the ad that had gone in the school newsletter; although he wasn't a parent himself, he is apparently a neighbour of a cousin of a parent. His name is Jonathan Perfrement. I asked him if he lived in the village, which he said he did, and whether he sang, which he said he didn't, but he thought that I could perhaps use some of his management expertise, saying he worked at the court house in Dellford as a senior operations manager. "I'm sure with a bit of blue-sky thinking we can start to really push the envelope here and develop some workable ways forward that'll help to enhance the product we can offer in the market place," he said. He's promised to turn up on Saturday week.

I tried phoning Charlie to see what he could tell me about Mr Perfrement but he was otherwise engaged so I rang Stan instead.

"Just don't even mention his name in Charlie's presence," Stan advised. "And if they do happen to find themselves in the same room together, have a sponge and a towel in the wings."

My heart sank. I really did not need any more conflicts among the membership than we had already. "How come?" I asked.

"He more or less single-handedly effected the closure of the court house in the village," said Stan. "And to this day Charlie's blamed me for it."

"What did you do?" I queried.

"He was giving us one of his lectures in management claptrapspeak," Stan said. "On good court management, and the need to strive to make improvements in the services we offered as a court house. He wanted to know what improvements we'd made here. He said something like 'We live in a very different world now, where considerations of strategic policy are dictated by the constraints of a performance culture driven in turn by the criteria that are ratcheted up on a regular basis and where those gearing the operation forward must be holistically motivated and adopt a directional purposive market-driven approach based upon sound indicators as to success or failure in any given sphere of activity.'"

"And what improvements had you made?" I asked him. "Close circuit TV? Witness video link facilities? Internet access for court users?"

"Well, not quite," Stan conceded. "But we had only the previous day ordered a new disinfectant tablet for the gents' urinal."

Maundy Thursday 20th March

Alan rang to ask whether I'd considered a leaflet drop round the village this weekend, which he said he'd be happy to help with. I conceded we had nothing to lose by trying it, despite the failure of my leaflet-dropping campaign in January. He gave me the details of a Steve Ramos, a printer in the village who could do the job for us quite cheaply, but warned me that his office might shut early for the Easter break.

Unfortunately I was forced to spend much of my time this morning on the phone to Angus and then the *Dellford Chronicle* querying what coverage

of the Assembly Room reopening we'd be getting in the paper. By the time I'd ascertained that the column space previously earmarked for us was being devoted partly to news of a controversial Transvestite Society inaugural night next weekend on our side of town, and partly to the story of Saffron Robertshaw in Priestfield Gardens whose pet rodents had succeeded in eating her father's passport the night before he was due to fly to the Balaerics, it was gone one o'clock and Mr Ramos' office was indeed shut. However, he had presciently left a mobile number on his answering machine message, and I was in luck; he said he was going away for Easter but I'd just caught him in time and he'd do the job for me this afternoon. Despite it being a very poor mobile line, I ascertained that he would, from material I emailed to him, print off really good quality colour leaflets at 5p per copy, but by way of a special seasonal offer for orders costing a minimum of £14 he would reduce his costs to just 1p per copy.
"So would you like the job done for that minimum price?" he asked me.
I considered. Fourteen hundred leaflets was probably a good deal more than we really needed, but considering for just a pound less I would get only two hundred and sixty, it struck me as an extra pound very well spent. And Alan was offering to help me out. So I asked for the increased quantity which Steve Ramos promised to deliver at home that evening.
When I arrived home Katie told me she had a little surprise for me. I hoped it might consist of a giant Smarties Easter egg, but chocolate was clearly the last thing on her mind as she opened the door of my study to reveal an invoice for £40 and a total of four thousand leaflets. But if I thought I was going to receive some sympathy from my loving wife for this latest cock-up, I very plainly had another think coming.
"Why don't you start delivering now?" she suggested with thinly-veiled sarcasm. "I'll come out with a cup of black coffee and a hot cross bun just after midnight."
That is, if my 3784 undelivered leaflets haven't joined the printed matter lining Saffron Robertshaw's guinea pigs' stomachs. And at the same time sent me seeking urgent and much needed solace in the Balaerics.

Easter Sunday 23rd March
A cloudy and dull Easter morning. As I arrived I saw Mr Culshaw getting his electric strimmer out of the boot of his car in readiness for an attack on the long tufty grass in the churchyard that was now only just dry enough to confront following last weekend's heavy rain.
It was perhaps the sheer impossibility of getting rid of four thousand leaflets that had dampened my enthusiasm for yesterday's distribution task, and I'd disposed of no more than about sixty. But today I not only managed to drop leaflets in each and every letterbox in Goatshanger Rise,

but with the permission of today's celebrant left copies in each pew in church for a packed Easter Sunday service. Immediately after the service I was buttonholed by Clive Radnedge, one of today's readers, who after hearing more about my venture said that as soon as he'd finished distributing the post-service champagne in the churchyard he'd make sure he recommended it to as many of the younger "Christmas and Easter" congregation members as he could. "I'd have been delighted to come myself," he said, "but once you heard my voice, you'd wish you hadn't bothered."
Inspired by a moving and faith-affirming Easter sermon, Clive's encouraging words and the fact that I managed to speak to at least seven people without upsetting any of them, I literally skipped out of the church this morning, gazing briefly heavenwards to thank the risen Lord for His goodness to me. It was only a pity that my heavenward glance should coincide with my arrival at an unscheduled obstruction in the form of the lead for Mr Culshaw's electric strimmer. In less time than it would have taken to say "Have a good trip" I was airborne and homing in on Clive Radnedge's delicate area which took the full force of an unintentional but particularly violent head butt. A moment later an aluminium tray, twenty-four glasses filled with champagne and three plates of assorted Asda nibbles had embarked on their own journey into space, landing with a series of earsplitting crashes on and around the church path and sending the hitherto joy-filled Easter worshippers hurrying for cover.
I only hope Mr Culshaw's strimmer is not allergic to Twiglets. And that Clive Radnedge wasn't planning on running in next Sunday's Dellford Half Marathon.

Tuesday 25th March

Left at just after midnight for my Love It FM interview in Markbury. I'd allowed plenty of time to get there, and as it happened I ended up with far too much, finding myself within three miles of the studio with two hours to spare. I managed to kill those two hours with a barely edible chickenburger at Giovanni's Eating Paradise – a caravan parked on a layby beside the A3949 – and the Junior Tricky Su Doku in the part of yesterday's *Sun* in which my chickenburger had been wrapped. I finally got to the main entrance of the Love It FM studios at just before five to three and confidently placed into the appropriate orifice a night entry pass that had been sent to me, only to be greeted by a robotic voice message "SORRY – DO NOT RECOGNISE. PLEASE TRY AGAIN." Having received this apology another twelve times and by then begun seriously to doubt its sincerity, I tried inserting the card upside down, back to front, and both upside down AND back to front, on the first two occasions receiving the same now scarcely tolerable expression of regret, and on the third occasion receiving the faintly sinister "ILLEGAL USAGE – REMOVE CARD IMMEDIATELY." After four laps of the building, during which I failed to find one single door that responded either to a discreet tug at the handle or a frustrated but undoubtedly satisfying kick, I moved to a strategic spot below the only lighted window in the building so I might resort to my own form of sophisticated state-of-the-art entry system: a three-hundred decibel yell. To my discomfiture this caused a series of ferocious barks to be unleashed on the hitherto still night air, and it was only the sight of a door opening and a beckoning ear-ringed youth that saved me from becoming instant Pedigree Chum substitute. "Don't mind him," the young man said, nodding in the direction of the latest auditioner for the lead canine in *The Hound Of The Baskervilles.* "That's only Radames The Seventh. Cheaper than a night security firm. And much more effective." I told him about the difficulties I'd had with the night pass. He looked at it cursorily and chuckled. "This expired eighteen months ago," he said. "Lord knows who sent it to you." I've no doubt He does. But at that moment I really didn't care whether it was the daughter of the newspaper roundsman for the controller of Love It FM on work experience, or the banqueting manager of the palace of Sheik Khalid Ashraf Rabin, seventy-third in line to the throne of the United Arab Emirates.

Mark Adam, when I finally got to meet him, was actually very pleasant and certainly appeared commendably interested in Saturday's do. However my tiredness, combined with the emotional and physical trauma that had attended my ill-fated attempts to enter the building, meant I didn't come over anything like as positively as I'd intended, and the uninterrupted thirty minutes we had seemed if anything slightly on the long side, with Mark actually doing more of the talking than I did. At three forty-five he thanked me for coming and put a record on, enabling him to usher me from the studio in person.

"Who's your next guest?" I asked him as we headed for the exit.

"Oh, there's nobody else tonight," he said. "I'll just carry on talking to myself till I'm relieved at half five. Or actually try to liven things up a bit by reading extracts from the local telephone directory. I doubt if my regular listeners will even notice. All six of them." I don't suppose he was being serious. But it was hardly calculated to make me feel any better about giving up a precious night's sleep and being subjected to Giovanni's unique method of salmonella redistribution.

On the way home, I put the radio on partially to try and keep myself awake and partially to see what expression and conviction Mark Adam would put into his recital of local chartered accountants and double glazing purveyors. Only to hear him provide a recap of my interview with him and tell his half-dozen loyal listeners – twice – that the gala reopening was happening on the 29th May. I thought about driving back to the studio to correct him, but decided that the prospect of losing six potential attenders on Saturday wasn't massively damaging. Well, not when compared with that of donating six pounds of flesh and bone, plus the seat of a perfectly good pair of trousers, to Radames The Seventh.

Saturday 29th March

The Assembly Room certainly did look very attractive in its redecorated state. The council had not only set aside money for the redecoration but for new kitchen fittings, crockery and utensils, signage throughout the building, and new furnishings and even pictures for the main hall and newly-converted committee room. Between them, Stan and Alan had chosen, ordered and taken delivery of it all, and we were to spend today putting it all in place in readiness for tonight's opening.

As so much of the work had already been done, and Alan had brought along two or three visiting friends to make up a very competent workforce, there was never any doubt that we'd make it in time, but it was still good to see so many very human qualities on display. First prize for eloquence would have to go to Charlie Tompkins, who on hearing Jonathan Perfrement was now unable to attend today, having apparently to give over his entire weekend to preparing for a Motivational Management And Strategic Skills Development Workshop on Monday, was moved to remark that his students could learn more about managing their motivation and developing their strategic skills through watching an episode of *Ivor The Engine.* The award for tenacity would have to go to Flora Sandstrom for putting up with over 2 hours of Charlie's spectacularly un-PC rhetoric, to say nothing of being addressed by him as Freya throughout that time, and holding out until six and a half minutes into the post-elevenses chukka, capitulating and retiring from the field of battle only when her tormentor looked down at her sandalled feet, sniffed audibly, and announced that he knew a first-rate chiropodist whose specialities were foot odours and verrucas. The agility medal was given to Stan, who on hearing Edna Mudge approach and threaten "summary execution" for the person who left a dirty copy of the *Sporting Life* on the new linoleum floor in the hallway, somehow managed to conceal himself in the new kitchen cupboard. And for the ingenuity medal, step forward Elphine Mapplebeck who managed to use a miniature version of the same Baby Belling cooker that had responded explosively to my attempts as a student to cook at over 5 degrees Fahrenheit above room temperature to produce so much roast chicken, bread sauce, gravy, stuffing, steamed treacle pudding and custard that as we began our afternoon work sessions in the red boiler suits donated by Alan we looked less like a team of eager

community volunteers than a fleet of Routemaster buses manoeuvring their way into the back yard of South Dalston depot.
But it soon became clear that amongst the respectable crowd of people who joined us tonight, there were virtually no potential singing members at all. Charlie brought along some Silly Old Buffers from Dellford, Flora brought along some humanists from Dellford, Alan brought along Debbie, her parents and her children from her previous marriage, Edna was there to ensure we were all out by ten and no later, and the Spadger was there to create more tedious column inches. Which just left one middle-aged man who didn't seem to belong to anybody, and who came in rather self-consciously after Alan had completed his entertainment and we had got going on our eats. I made a point of going up to him and introducing myself.
"I hope I've come to the right place," he said. "To be honest, I'm quite relieved to see how normal everyone looks."
"Well, we try not to stick out too much in a crowd," I laughed, "although I know it can be hard sometimes. We tend to be a bit exhibitionist by nature, I suppose. Those of us who are used to it, anyway."
"I'm interested you're mixed sex," he said. "Is it normal for men and women to work together for this sort of thing?"
"Perfectly," I said. "We may consider splitting into male and female on occasions but mostly we'll all be working in the one room."
"And do you intend to do a lot of performing in public?"
"As much as possible," I said, "That's what this is all about."
I saw him looking distinctly worried. "What if we just want to do it – you know – mostly by ourselves? Using your group just to give people a bit more confidence to do that?"
It seemed a fair point. "Well, yes, part of this is about gaining in self-confidence," I said. "It's the sort of thing which if you do lots of, you do start to believe in yourself more. But the predominant aim is for all the members to show off their assets and their skills to the punters."
With horror now clearly visible on his face, he beckoned me away from the others and said in a loud whisper "This *is* the inaugural Transvestite Society meeting, isn't it?"

Sunday 30th March
At church this morning instead of a sermon there was a talk by Phyllis Aughterlonie who lives in the village and who told us about a project she was helping to set up, seeking to establish a night refuge for homeless people in Dellford. Apparently it is far more of a problem than anybody realised.
"Imagine," she said, "as you go back to your warm homes tonight, there will be at least twenty people, some as old as seventy or eighty, sleeping

out on streets just ten minutes' drive away. Rain or cold, wind or snow, sleet or hail."

It was certainly one of the more powerful addresses I'd heard, and I was in quite a thoughtful mood for the rest of the service, wondering to myself how I could best contribute to her excellent cause. Fortuitously, I found myself standing next to her in the coffee queue afterwards and told her I'd be pleased to assist her charity in whatever way I could, starting perhaps by making a donation to her funds.

"That would be very kind," she said. "Especially as one of our fund raising team's in quite a bad way at the moment. A nasty accident he sustained in church last Sunday."

I asked if that was Clive Radnedge by any chance.

"That's right," said Phyllis. "And it couldn't have come at a worse time for him. It's only six days away now."

"What's that?" I asked.

"His wedding night," said Phyllis.

When I got back from church there was fantastic news. Alan told me we have our first new recruits, both male – Mike Rowbotham and Jack Kellaway. Apparently they love close harmony singing including swingle and barbershop, they both live in the village, both are in their early forties with plenty of years left before they become singing liabilities rather than assets, they have many years' experience of singing in choirs and small groups, they have children who have just left home meaning they don't have family responsibilities as such during the evenings, and they're looking for new challenges. They're free and available almost every night. To borrow from Jonathan Perfrement's lexicon, they tick every box there is.

"So when did they contact you?" I asked.

"Last night, after you'd gone," said Alan. "and we've got that ghastly Edna Mudge to thank for it. The one who proudly told me her sole musical connection was the electric plug she used to get radio 2."

"How's that?" I asked.

"She was the one who stuffed Stan's *Sporting Life* down the gas boiler having found it on the kitchen draining board," Alan explained. "Mike and Jack were the emergency heating engineers we had to call out to stop the whole place going up in smoke."

APRIL

Tuesday 1st April

Stan rang me at work this morning to tell me he had some good news. "I've got another singer for you," he said. "I was doing some tidying up in the Assembly Room on Sunday and she came in having heard the thing you did on the radio on Tuesday thinking the opening was that evening not Saturday. Lives locally, really keen to get involved in something like you're organising. And she's got a friend who'd like to come along too."
"Sounds brilliant," I said. "What's the catch?"
"There's no catch," said Stan. "I've got some contact details, and all you need to do is phone her. Failing that, she and her friend usually come to the pub on Sunday lunchtime with their husbands."
"Go on," I said. "What's her name and number?"
"Her name's Ali Forlop," said Stan. He went on to give me what was clearly a Lambsball Green number.
Unfortunately the number he gave me was constantly engaged, but after my seventh unsuccessful attempt I suddenly realised what Ali Forlop was an anagram of. Hardly the most sophisticated piece of seasonal trickery, but I suppose I deserved it. After all, I was the one who had initially delivered Stan's *Sporting Life* into Edna Mudge's unforgiving custody last Saturday.
When I got home there was a letter waiting for me, and this really was good news. It was from a Laura Dublin of 28 The Meadows at the south end of the village telling me she'd read the two-line piece Angus Spadgwick had written previewing Saturday's events, was really sorry she'd missed the do on Saturday owing to a writers' convention in Tamworth, had just moved into the village, was an experienced singer in her late thirties, was looking for a choir to join and was really keen to join the group. She went on to say she'd be at home on Thursday night between seven thirty and eight thirty and she'd be pleased for me to pop round to see her provided that was convenient to me and that I could confirm a suitable time by email; it had to be email apparently as she was waiting for her phone to be connected and her mobile had been stolen. I was slightly surprised by her email address which did not contain the words "Laura" or "Dublin" but that was no business of mine. Anyway, I emailed her to say how much I was looking forward to coming round to see her and that I was sure that if she was up for it and had sufficient experience and ability, she was just what I was after and it would be really good to work with her.
Having now heard from what would be our first female recruit, I now felt quite frustrated that there was no way of making more immediate contact with her. Still, I could at least establish her history and credentials as a

writer which had led her to give up a Saturday to enrich the good people of Tamworth. Accordingly, I got onto the Amazon website.....and traced a grand total of one book that appeared to be attributable to a Laura Dublin that was in print. *Psychosocial Trends In Acquisitive Criminal Activity In Guatemala, 1874 to 1956,* published last year by the University of Chicago Press, 69 dollars 95 cents. Astonishingly, some copies still available.

Thursday 3rd April

Well, it seems our Saturday night gala opening has yielded more interest than I thought. I had a phone call today from a lady named Cecily Baverstock, who said that she and a number of friends of hers from the now defunct Lambsball Green WI were interested in joining our group. "There's just one thing," she said. "We're all in our sixties and seventies."

That certainly is a problem. Although we might run into trouble from the age discrimination lobby if I set a maximum age limit, we'd agreed at committee that we would subtly try and discourage those whose good singing years were behind them – if anywhere. I rang Alan and he agreed with me that the fairest way to root out any no-hopers was a fairly rigorous voice test for each aspiring singer. I rang Cecily back and asked her together with her camp followers to come along on Monday week at seven.

There was better news, however, on the concert planning front. My conscience had been seriously troubled ever since Sunday by my having deprived Phyllis Aughterlonie of potential revenue she'd hoped to generate from one of her star fundraisers. Accordingly I rang her tonight and asked if she'd like us to do a concert in aid of her night refuge project. She not only gratefully accepted but said we were welcome to perform in her garden; in return she would provide substantial refreshments and would guarantee us an audience using her extensive network of contacts. We've agreed the 28th June.

Then, of course, it was off tonight to meet Laura Dublin. I'd never visited The Meadows before but despite the early onset of darkness with thick cloud and rain in the air, I found it easily enough. It was, I have to say, a rather unprepossessing cul-de-sac consisting chiefly of rundown council properties, while in front of them stood an inordinate number of dilapidated parked vehicles providing potentially rich pickings for road tax enforcement officers endeavouring to meet their month's performance targets. Somewhat incongruously, near the end on the right-hand side in a gap between portions of the council housing, bang next to number 28, there was a large sign advertising THE GABLES – SUPERLATIVE BEAUTIFULLY DESIGNED FOUR BEDROOM HOMES ENJOYING

ALL MODERN LUXURIES AND COMFORTS – PART EXCHANGE CONSIDERED, MORE LAND URGENTLY REQUIRED. It wasn't hard to imagine how heartfelt the last part of the notice must have been. Number 28 wasn't far off being the most ramshackle of all the properties on The Meadows, but I was interested in the singer, not the bricks and mortar, so edging round a large puddle and the remains of an early 70s Ford Granada that littered the front garden, and vaulting nimbly over a half portion of sofa bed, I made my way to the front door and gripped the door knocker – only for the wretched thing to come away in my hand. By now it was raining hard and after several minutes of zero response to a number of crisply-delivered raps to the door using the now detached knocker, I was about to call it a day. At that moment, however, I heard the slow clump of footsteps inside make a dramatic crescendo from *mezzo piano* to *fortissimo*, and the door swung open to reveal a woman for whom the term "morbidly obese" might have been perceived as unduly flattering. She stood there glowering and wheezing at me for a few seconds, then breathlessly asked how she could help me. I wondered if even the four words she used might prove too much and was afraid I may be called upon to flag down the next ten-ton truck that might chance to be heading in the direction of the Dellford municipal mortuary.

"I'm – er – looking for Laura Dublin," I said.

"No Laura Dublin here," she spluttered. She somehow manoeuvred her body ninety degrees to the port side. "EDNA!" she yelled. "Man here asking for Laura Dublin. Do we know Laura Dublin?" A shiver went down my spine at the mention of the word Edna and my worst fears were confirmed when, despite the fact that the massive form in front of me prevented anything but the most token view of what lay behind, I saw the Assembly Room cleaner approach, her face a picture of feral ferocity. Within seconds I was being angrily upbraided for having had the audacity to interrupt their Thursday cribbage night and would I leave now before Phoebe set Samba on me.

I had no idea who or what Samba was. But when, having cleared the sofa bed and the Ford Granada and skirted round the water jump, I heard a rustling and what sounded like a strangled yowl from the bushes to the right of the garden path, I realised I was likely to be about to find out. Desperate to avoid a confrontation with a creature that could have been Phoebe's pet ferret or a black panther on the loose from the Cuddly World Wildlife Park six miles away, I shot away to the left, leaving the front garden of number 28 and heading resolutely for The Gables. Or to be more precise, a large expanse of liquid mud. As the yowling behind me intensified I forged forward, seeing some smoother ground ahead and jumping onto it with relief; relief that was shortlived, as the ground seemed to give way underneath and I found myself collapsing into a grey

gooey mass that could have been cement, plaster or overcooked bread sauce.
Thankfully the kindly occupants of number 30 managed to pull me out in time to prevent me spending the rest of my existence languishing amongst the foundations of a superlative beautifully designed four bedroom home enjoying all modern luxuries and comforts, part exchange considered, more land urgently required. Plus of course the bonus of a motor museum and dangerous animal rescue centre less than thirty yards from the front door.

Sunday 6th April

After Thursday's debacle I'd not surprisingly gone down with a stinking cold and today was the first day I felt vaguely human again. I couldn't face church this morning and was going to suggest to Katie that we had a long walk and tea out somewhere when the phone rang. It was Stan asking us both out for a pre-lunch drink as a peace offering, telling me there were a couple of "attractive young singers" he wanted me to meet. I told Stan his spoof last Tuesday morning hadn't upset me at all and really there was nothing to apologise for, but I certainly wasn't going to turn down the chance of a free drink. So to the Welldiggers we went.
Stan greeted us warmly and introduced me to Karen Milton and.....Alison Forlop. Both were, they told me, in their early thirties; both had happened to hear me on the radio but hadn't made it to last Saturday's opening; both lived in the village and, as mums with young children, both were keen to get out, meet people and revive their enthusiasm for regular choral singing which they'd given up during pregnancy.
It was all excellent news, and with the aid of my mobile we quickly arranged to meet with Alan and our other new singers later in the week, but I simply could not wait to get Stan out of earshot of them both and tell him I thought the Ali Forlop thing was an April Fool prank in revenge for the *Sporting Life* business.
"Not that," he said. "It was that ridiculous letter I sent you supposedly from Laura Dublin. But obviously you wouldn't have been stupid enough to fall for that. You know, believe anyone had actually not only read but acted on something Agatha Splingewick had written. And go round to Phoebe Cockleridge's house and interrupt her Thursday girls' night in with Edna Mudge. Suicide."
I couldn't believe what I'd just heard. "I d-didn't think it was a joke," I stammered. "I just assumed I'd misread the address."
"Ah well," Stan said with a smile. "As long as you didn't try to send Laura Dublin an email."
I thought back to the effusive communication I'd sent her with its references to my looking forward to seeing her, and her being up for it

and just what I was after. But I wasn't going to give Stan the satisfaction of knowing any of that. So I simply smiled and shook my head.
"That's all right," said Stan. "She's not renowned for her sense of humour."
"I don't understand," I said. "I thought you'd made her up."
"Oh, there's nothing made-up about Laura Dublin," said Stan, fingering the top of his beer glass with a smirk. "She's real enough. As wife of the chair of the Dellford Bench, headmistress of Dellford Girls' High School, president of the Dellford branch of the Mothers Union, senior elder of the Dellford Baptist Church and secretary to the Dellford Temperance Society."

Wednesday 9th April
A landmark day: our first singers' meeting, at Alan's house. Admittedly there are only the six of us so far, including Alan and myself, and although I somehow can't see us managing Bach's *B Minor Mass* or Mahler's *Symphony Of A Thousand*, it is certainly sufficient for some four-part harmony. I was a bit uneasy that none of the rest of those who had been present at the earlier meetings – Charlie, Flora, Stan, Elphine and Angus – were being invited, but Alan made the point that the object of tonight's meeting was to consider what and where we might sing rather than anything else. "Plus," Alan said to me surreptitiously, "if Ali and Karen actually have to meet any of that lot on their first evening with us, we might never see them again." We've agreed that even though none of the original contingent besides Alan and myself are at all anxious to sing, we'll all have to meet together at some stage and put things on a slightly more formal footing. Even though I shudder at the thought of a constitution and a committee, if we're promoting ourselves as a community organisation we have to do things properly. We've agreed to meet all together at the Assembly Room in a week's time at 7.30, being joined by our new committee member Jonathan Perfrement providing, he says, his all-day Good Time Management And Achieving Appropriate Work-Life Balance Strategic Working Sub Group meeting finishes no later than six thirty.
We spent a very convivial evening discussing possible venues and concert ideas in addition to the booking we'd secured ten days ago. A church concert was mooted, as was the idea of using one of the many halls in Dellford, although I am still anxious to keep it local at this stage. Ali was full of good suggestions and mentioned one venue in the village I'd overlooked, namely the Dolls House Exhibition in Clarke Street which opens only in the summer months. She said it has a reasonable-sized exhibition hall which would be ideal for concerts.

"Well, we can try," said Alan with a sigh, "but I've performed there three times, and each time it was a disaster."
"How come?" Karen enquired.
"The first one was a meeting of the now defunct Lambsball Green WI," said Alan. "Bucketing with rain and blowing a gale, my first item Gilbert & Sullivan's *How Beautifully Blue The Sky*, hole in the ceiling, abandoned at half time owing to waterlogged pitch. The second was a supper in aid of museum funds. I was supposed to be doing 45 minutes at the end, six people were violently sick because the starters hadn't been cooked properly, supper didn't end till ten to midnight and I was faded out after two and a half minutes having sung just one verse of *Food Glorious Food*. The third was the worst. From St Cuthbert's School a couple of miles out, Cultural Awareness Project or something of the sort. The year nines were the worst. Shouting, yelling, slow handclaps, catcalls, booing, rotten tomatoes, paper darts. Horrendous."
"Weren't there any teachers with them?" I asked.
"Oh, yes," said Alan. "They were the ones throwing the rotten tomatoes."

Friday 11th April

Today's post brought the spring newsletter of the Lambsball Green Dippers, of which I'd become a member following my unceremonious ducking on New Year's Day. It included a photograph of this inauspicious event – apparently I have the distinction of being the first and only person who's decided to be initiated in the well rather than in the goldfish pond – as well as news of future events, details of those among the surprisingly large membership who have undergone career or house moves, and the places of the aforementioned members in the Dippers' pecking order, whatever those mean. I can only say that I don't know how I have got through the last three months of my life without realising that Shaun Culpepper(Second Dipper) is now admissions manager of the Ear, Nose and Throat Clinic of St Columba's Hospital, Hobart, or that Calvin Hucklecote(Deputy Sturgeon) has risen to the dizzy heights of fleet manager of the Happy Coach Company based in Market Drayton. The next big event is the Fish Quiz at the Welldiggers on 16th May. Each year the quiz has a theme linked to fish: this year's is yet to be announced, but apparently recent themes have included the film *Jaws* and the Birds Eye product range. If it helps to get me some more recruits, it may be worth my while turning up – as long as nobody's expecting me to take part. I've never much cared for fish fingers, still less studied the ingredients list on one of the packets.
A separate piece of paper informed me that my first half-yearly subscription should have been paid in March and is now four weeks overdue. This was the first I heard that any subscription was payable at

all. But I may as well cough up. For one thing, I don't at this stage wish to compromise my chances of being admitted to the quiz evening especially if I may find some new singers among the participants. And I should hate to think that I might cease to receive the newsletter and thereby fail to hear whether Dean Wateringbury (First Troutman) succeeds in getting the job of senior night security officer at Heckmondwike Ice Hockey Club.

Sunday 13th April

As we were leaving church this morning I was approached by a portly but pleasant-looking woman in late middle age.

"I've heard all about your new singing group," she said, "and I'm delighted because I think there's something you could do to help us."

She told me she was a tireless worker for the Samaritans in and around Dellford, and they were extremely anxious for more funding. She's asked if we will do a programme of about 60 minutes of preferably light-hearted singing, either *a cappella* or with piano, during early June, in the church. The local fundraising team will do all the publicity; all we need to do is turn up, sing for them, enjoy a glass of wine and some nibbles, and we'll get a small donation to put towards either a charity of our choice or to further our own organisation. Couldn't be better.

"That'll be fine," I said confidently. "And your name is….."

"Dublin," she replied. "Laura Dublin."

The room seemed to swim before my eyes. Mechanically I took a note of her actual address – another world away from 28 The Meadows, Lambsball Green – as well as her phone number, then made my excuses and left as quickly as I could, thinking the less said about that previous email the better. During the afternoon, however, I found myself having second thoughts, and felt that if we were to work together closely on the Samaritans concert, I needed to clear the air and apologise straight away. After all, this would be our inaugural performance as a singing group, and the last thing I wanted to do was start on the wrong foot and risk ruining our reputation for good. Finally, with dry throat, quivering hands and a veritable army of cabbage-whites and Red Admirals having a field day in my interior, I reached for my mobile and phoned Laura Dublin.

"I just want to say," I said, "I'm really so sorry about that email."

"What email?" she asked.

"The one I sent the other week. You know, about hoping you were up for it and being just what I was after. It was a stupid misunderstanding. I was the victim of a prank."

"I've never received any email from you," she said, sounding rather irritable. "What address did you send it to?"

I duly retrieved the original mail from my system and told her.

"That isn't my email address," she said frostily.
Having brought that conversation to a spluttering and red-faced conclusion, wasted no time in phoning Stan.
"So," I said, "if that wasn't her email address, whose is it?"
"Edna Mudge," said Stan.

Monday 14th April

Voice tests tonight for the first crop of applicants. Alan and I were doing the testing, and Alan's wife Debbie kindly came along to make up a panel of three. We felt out of fairness that we should test Mike, Jack, Karen and Ali, and as expected they were formalities: excellent voices and excellent readers. Then we moved to the ex-WI contingent and the fun started.
First on: Cecily Baverstock, offering us *O For The Wings Of A Dove*. Which we decided would need clipping after the briefest of flights. "Not quite what we're looking for," Alan said with a diplomatic smile.
Next: Ruby Chetnole, rashly attempting *Pie Jesu* from Faure's *Requiem*. At least, it started that way but as it went on it metamorphosed – I wouldn't say entirely effortlessly – into *Pie Jesu* from Andrew Lloyd Webber's *Requiem* before slipping back into Faure-esque mode shortly before the whistle blew for full time. "Not entirely suited to our style," Alan said graciously.
Third on the list: Coral Fullilove, with some light operatic relief in the form of *Poor Wand'ring One* from *The Pirates Of Penzance*. Her big mistake: thinking she knew the words. I did know the words, having sung it in a school production at the age of 14, but even a twelve-eyed nine-footed humanoid from one of the more obscure satellites of Uranus who believed Gilbert & Sullivan to be a London department store would have realised that the librettist utilised more words in the six pages we endured than Poor, Wandering, One, La, La and La. "We think perhaps your special brand of talent is better deployed elsewhere," said Alan with a sage grin.
Fourth and penultimately: Ivy Williams, who perhaps wisely restricted her choice to the National Anthem. Her cardinal error: ignoring the rule "less is more." She got through the first verse without difficulty. The second verse proved harder to negotiate, and she picked up a double fault early on. Into the final verse, and following an initially mistimed volley she slammed her attempted recovery into the net; her next shot was pronounced by the line judge to be long, and the umpire, despite a vigorous challenge, was not minded to overrule the call. "We think," said Alan sympathetically, "we'd have difficulty slotting you into the existing line-up."
Finally: Wanda Phinnikirk. Brimming with complete lack of confidence, and giving herself an out by saying she'd lost her voice, she launched into

what indeed was an all but tuneless dying scene from a work she described as "Deedo and Aeeda." Whether intended to be from *Aida* or from *Dido and Aeneas*, I'm not sure, but I'd witnessed more heartfelt dying scenes on the terraces at Wolverhampton Wanderers. As she hoarsely whimpered towards her final demise, Alan whispered into my ear "Sorry. I've run out of the polite comments." With an exasperated clap of his hand, he screwed into a tight ball the piece of paper in front of him and said "Sorry, Mrs Phinnigook, I can't bear it any more. That was absolutely awful." Prompting Wanda to let out a horrified squawk and collapse into an ungainly heap on the ground.
"Now that's what I call a dying scene," said Alan.

Wednesday 16th April
The post today brought a curt letter signed by all those who had failed their voice test on Monday saying that they found our rejections callous and cruel and that we could expect little or no support from former WI members of Lambsball Green or their friends. I can't say I'm heartbroken. Seeing that I never really wanted them in the first place.
We were a full house for our meeting tonight: Alan, our four singing recruits, Stan, Charlie, Flora, Jonathan, Elphine, Angus and myself. Jonathan Perfrement, an immaculately-dressed, fresh-faced man in his early thirties, just out of a meeting with the Strategic Taskforce Implementation Manager, was perfectly pleasant, and I admired his ability to drink a carton of Starbucks coffee in one hand and fire off a succession of emails into his Black Berry with another, in response to the 28 mails he claimed to have received during his walk from the Assembly Room car park.
After coffee and Elphine's very tasty home-made biscuits, of which despite having four each we still failed to get beyond the top of the first of nine layers, we got down to business. We decided to name ourselves the Lambsball Green Singers for now; no prizes for originality, but we hope to come up with a punchier and more original name in the coming months. There will be a committee, including a representative from the singers among them, meeting as required and charged with responsibility for recruitment, maintenance of accounts, future bookings and liaison with other organisations; singing rehearsals will take place independently of committee meetings, again as needed, and indeed we've fixed up our first rehearsal to take place in just over a fortnight, working towards the two engagements we've already got during June; and all members will pay a subscription, principally to finance the ordering of music. All of that agreed, the four new singers left, and we convened our first "official" committee meeting and set about allocating duties. Alan has very kindly agreed to act as chairman, leaving me as secretary, treasurer, librarian

and, until I get a volunteer from among the ranks, singer representative. Alan duly took the chair and commenced by asking the others present what they felt they themselves could add to the committee.
"I'll tell you where I stand," said Charlie. "I'm a busy man, and I feel I've got you started with the contacts I've suggested for you. So I think I'll take a back seat as far as running the group is concerned, but I'd like to attend committee meetings effectively as representative of the village and just keep an eye on how things go. What about you, Fatima?"
Flora didn't even bother to correct him. "Well, as you probably know, I've my own agenda in a sense," she said. "I'm still after more members for my Humanist Society, which as you know is the only other community group in the village and now has a regular and loyal membership."
"Exactly," said Charlie. "I met him walking home last night."
Wisely, Flora chose to plough on. "Anyhow," she said, "Following a session with my life coach, I've also plans to establish a yoga and meditation group in the village and I see my role here as using my contacts in both camps, as it were, to help both my groups and this one to thrive. I have a vision for this village as a humanist model, where residents are able to share, interact and empathise with each other, bound by a holistic concern for each other's welfare independent of any religious thought process or philosophy. I've given a great deal of thought to my role and how it might be titled, and having reflected upon it at length I would wish to nominate myself as Community Outreach Partner, or C.O.P if you prefer."
There was a pause as we all digested this worthy speech, broken only by Charlie who simply chuckled and said "It's a fair COP, eh, Fatima?"
I really don't know why she puts up with it.
"Let's move on to Angus," said Alan diplomatically."How can you help us?"
"I don't propose to play a part in committee affairs," said Angus. "I would however be pleased to serve you as press officer and report your activity in my column accordingly."
"There's just one problem," muttered Charlie. "What will we do if we actually want anyone to read it?"
"Thank you, Charlie," said Alan. "Well, save for Elphine, whose contribution and support are hugely appreciated, that just leaves Stan and Jonathan. Now, I've spoken to Stan who's happy to be our Assembly Room rep. He had to leave us just before the meeting started, I'm afraid."
"Why was that?" Angus asked.
"He'd left a couple of dirty cups out after the Humanist Society met on Monday night." Alan replied, "and having thought Edna Mudge was

away in London, saw her face at the window. He was enquiring if anyone knew the time of the next flight to Dar-es-Salaam."
"What about you, Mr Perfrement?" said Charlie to Jonathan, who had said nothing whatsoever up to this point, but had had his head buried in his laptop.
"I've listened carefully to the discussions," Jonathan replied, "and applaud the blue-sky thinking, but feel that what you have here demands a focussed management approach which is why I have in mind placing myself in the position of Performance Manager, largely replicating a key aspect of what I do in my professional life. While you've been talking, I've prepared a document which I'll email to you all in due course. It provides a number of alternative frontloaded corporate bases for a focussed target-orientated approaches to service delivery matching organisational competence-based headline requirements to people and market strategies for a structure-driven strategic model which if successfully implemented in partnership with other relevant agencies and stakeholders and promises to optimise all aspects of performance that will significantly enhance your overall product."
There was a stunned silence. Broken only by Charlie who turned to me and observed "I think it means 'my postillion has just been struck by lightning.'"

Sunday 20th April

Today was the vicar's first Sunday back following his long absence through illness. Rejoicing in the name of Geraint Collymore, he was a tall, thin man boasting curly, snowy-white hair and glasses with one of the earpieces supported by sellotape. I was quite impressed with his intonations and wondered if he might be interested in joining our group. But I was very disappointed with his sermon, a rather wordy and intellectual address which might have gone down well in a theological college but was far too heavy for a village congregation whose members were preoccupied with rather weightier spiritual and moral considerations such as the appropriate oven setting for the Sunday roast or the length of grass on the front lawn. I was however pleased when, having got to the end, he said "Before we move on, just a word to the youngsters." I don't think I was the only one who looked round to see who might qualify under this head, assuming, by youngsters, one discounted anyone above the age of fifty. In fairness there were three in the congregation who had not yet attained majority, so arguably the vicar was justified in making the effort, albeit one of the trio was an infant in arms, one was a two-year-old who was breakfasting on the 1926 First Edition Introduction to *Hymns Of Praise*, and the third, a lanky youth of about fourteen sitting in front of me with his parents, seemed more interested in the array of substances that had taken up residence under the nail of his middle finger. But my happy anticipation of a dynamic and relevant message was quickly dulled when this part of the address began, and I found myself wondering whether he had any ability at all to relate to the 49-and-under category. I don't suppose any of those present had a real interest in 1980's pop, so reference to the iconic singers Alvin Costello, Michael George and Maradonna could safely be said to have gone over their heads. An eyebrow might have been raised slightly, no more, when he invoked the name of the fictional hero Gary Potter. But one can only hope that it was just a slip of the tongue that caused him, in support of one of his arguments, to cite the famous Spanish footballer, Victoria Beckham.

Afterwards I introduced myself to him and told him about my new initiative. He seemed very impressed, said he'd give us every support, and indicated he might be interested in joining the singers. "Since I became vicar here ten years ago we've never had anything like this," he said. "You must come round to the rectory and tell me more about what you've got in mind." He took me aside, and said in a conspiratorial voice, "Do you know, it was only the other week we were saying that it must have been at least twenty years that the village had its own choral society. Sad loss."

"Well, not according to a guy I was talking to the other day," I said, recalling a conversation I'd had with Stan in the pub. "He said the man who was running it was – how can I put it – mentally a little unstable. Rather gone off the rails." I hardly liked to tell a man of the cloth that Stan had actually described the choirmaster as a 'seam short of a shag pile.'

"Probably just as well there's a new man at the helm now, then, isn't there?" the vicar said with a smile.

Stan phoned me later to agree a couple of Assembly Rooms bookings. "Funny," I said to him. "The vicar, Geraint Collymore, reminded me of the choral society they used to have here. Whose choirmaster you said only last week was a sandwich short of a shagpile, or words to that effect."

"Oh yes," said Stan.

"Just out of interest, what did you say his name was?" I enquired.

"Geraint Collymore," said Stan.

Monday 21st April

To Dellford Choral Society's Guest Evening.

My spirits sank almost immediately I entered the gymnasium of Dellford Boys' High School. It reeked of an unpleasant mixture of floor polish and stale sweat, and it was also freezing cold. Although it was supposed to be a 7.30 kick-off, and I'd rushed my dinner to be there on time, only two or

three others had got there before me and it wasn't till ten to eight that an ageing man with a bushy grey beard and glasses with severe black frames suggested to the 50 or 60 or so who were now present that it was perhaps time we made a start. A quick look around the gymnasium confirmed the paucity of those aged under 55, the only one who fell into the 50-and-under category – and that by only a few years, I guessed – being a large red-faced greasy-haired man who looked like an escapee from the top end of platform 13 at Clapham Junction. We began proceedings with a full 15 minutes of vocal exercises which the grey-beard insisted on putting us through before we looked at any actual music. But, at length, copies of Faure's *Requiem*, a piece I've never really got on with, were distributed and we turned to the Kyrie at the start of the work. That was at five past eight. By a quarter to nine, when a break for refreshment and notices was called, we had covered precisely four pages. The experience was made none the pleasanter by the appallingly raucous sounds emanating from our friend the trainspotter, who had taken up a position just two places to the left of me. The cigarette smell on his huge silver-coloured coat, adding to the general stench list, was almost as repellent as his voice.
Things seemed to look up marginally at break-time when we were invited to adjourn to an adjacent room in which wine, fruit juice and sandwiches were served and potential new members were asked to make themselves known to the secretary. She appeared to be, if anything, slightly above the average age of the assembled company, but she certainly seemed efficient enough, handing me a "New Members' Pack" consisting of a rehearsal schedule, a copy of the society's constitution and rules, an extraordinarily complex table of subscriptions, fees and levies, a booklet headed "Concert Dress And Decorum" and details of the extensive schedule of social functions, from the annual Tea Dance and Bridge Drive at the Dellford Waldorf Hotel to the society's annual Weekend Knees Up in Prestatyn *(£85 deposits must be with Doris by 1st May or you will not be guaranteed your place on the coach*).
"You were the one who rang up, weren't you?" she said to me as she relieved me of my £2.50p rehearsal levy. "Wanting to know if any Lambsball Green residents are among our number."
"That's right," I said.
"Well," she said with a beaming smile, "There's good news and bad news. The bad news is that there's only one of our number who is."
My heart sank. I'd hoped that there might be half a dozen at least.
"The good news," she went on, "is that he's here tonight, and I'm sure he'll be just the man for you. He's very keen to do more singing in his home village, really very committed……there he is! Gregory!"
In answer to her call, a man swung round in her direction. To my absolute horror, I saw it was the greasy-haired tenor whose voice would have

sounded discordant in an assembly of drunken parakeets. "Gregory," said the secretary. "This is Mr Braithwaite. He's set up a little choral group in your village and would be very keen for you to join him."
"That's splendid," he responded, shaking my hand painfully hard and exhaling a generous helping of nicotine. "I was told the other night that you didn't need any more tenors. I'm so glad I'm mistaken."
"Actually," I began, "I'm afraid...."
"I'll tell you," he said, taking me aside and thereby exposing me to the full force of the smell emanating from his hygienically challenged underarms. "This is marvellous. I'm a single man, always have been. I don't have many friends....don't have any friends in the village really. I'm stuck in a flat in Baker Crescent and can't afford to move. It's been really hard for me these last few years. I'm just so pleased that there's something going on in the village now that I can get involved with. Help get my life back on track. So when do I turn up?"
In the circumstances, felt I had no choice but to tell him, then wasted little time in placing the new members' pack on one side and making a swift exit.
Having got home earlier than anticipated I suggested to Katie we had a quick drink in the pub. I certainly felt I needed it. Stan was in there, and I told him where I'd been earlier in the evening.
"The choral society?" he said. "You didn't meet Greg Corbally, did you? The guy with the BO and that awful thick puffa jacket stinking of cheap ciggies?"
"Yes," I said.
"Oh, crumbs," said Stan. "I've been doing everything I can to keep him away from your new group. If I've put him off once I've put him off a dozen times. Been dreading him turning up uninvited. You've not asked him along, have you?"
I could hardly bring myself to confess. "Still," I said, trying to convince myself more than Stan, "he could be quite a useful singer. He's certainly very keen."
"Put it this way," said Stan. "I can't think of anybody else who might have managed to single-handedly provoke the resignation of five out of the last six conductors of the Dellford Choral Society."
"That still leaves one who stayed the course," I said.
"Not quite," said Stan. "He shot himself."

Wednesday 23rd April

I'd spent some time last night looking through my music collection to see what we could sing at our first meeting next week. Unfortunately I'd got rid of a lot of stuff during our house move and most of my madrigal books and other collections for unaccompanied choirs, which I'd fondly

accumulated during my membership of the Wolverhampton Polytechnic Glee Club, had disappeared. This morning I phoned Dellford Music Supplies and asked them if they had any suitable collections. Having been invited to "bear with me just one sec" by the young woman who answered, I waited for ten minutes before being told that it was really the lady in charge I ought to speak to and could I ring back tomorrow when she was back in the shop.
"What's her name?" I asked.
"Margharita-Helene Dawes-Finkleton," the young woman replied.
Reflecting that just asking to speak to her tomorrow would be testing my oral communication skills to the limit, to say nothing of doubling my phone bill for the current quarter, I decided on another tack. This evening I phoned Frank Tripplehorn, my old choirmaster. Unfortunately I caught him in the middle of an important prior engagement, namely *The Simpsons* on Channel 4, but he told me Joan Trumpington was still the choir librarian and suggested I called her. I did think any remaining marbles she had would have well and truly sunk into oblivion after all this time, but nothing ventured nothing gained, as they say, so I gave her a ring. I explained why I was calling – to look at the current contents of the vestry cupboard – and asked if I might pop round sometime in the next few days to check it out.
"The current contents?" she said.
"Yes," I confirmed. "Of the vestry cupboard."
"That's fine," she said at once. "I would warn you though, it is rather difficult to get at."
"Don't worry about that," I said, pleasantly surprised that she seemed reasonably on the ball. "I take it it's worth looking at?"
"Oh yes," said Joan. "I don't think anyone's looked it over for a long time. I'm pleased you've grasped the nettle. I've been meaning to do something about it for ages myself."
"The only thing is, I may be a bit of time," I said.
"Oh, take as long as you like," said Joan. "I'll be waiting to give you the key to the cupboard, and you can just let me have it when you leave. I should warn you, though, it's a bit untidy in there, but don't worry if you make a mess. I can clear it up later."
"And when can I come round?" I asked. "I thought about six on Friday if that's convenient."
"That's fine," said Joan. I couldn't believe it. I'd expected this conversation to last at least an hour. "So just to check I've got this straight, that's six o'clock on Friday....Mr...."
"Braithwaite," I said. "David Braithwaite."

"Thank you," she said. "I'll just write that down.....Mr David Braithwaite....six o'clock on Friday....vestry broom cupboard to read the electricity meter."
So Margharita-Helene Dawes Finkleton it is then.

Sunday 27th April
Decided to give church a miss this morning, enjoying a relaxed morning and a pleasant early afternoon walk before meeting the vicar for tea at four.
I'd assumed Geraint was a single man, but after opening the door to me he introduced me to his wife Nancy, who has been far from well herself over the past few months. We then sat down to an excellent tea and I gave them both a resume of my progress in establishing the singing group.
After tea Geraint took me into the room he called the Old Scullery and showed me what he described as the "biggest collection of bus memorabilia in the county." There were literally hundreds of photographs and picture postcards of buses, ancient and modern, adorning the walls; a glass case inside which was a massive assortment of old bus tickets; tables on which were albums full of newspaper cuttings and photographs of buses; and shelves upon shelves of bus timetables. Had I wanted to know the time of the first bus from Halifax to Bradford tomorrow, Newquay to Bodmin next week, or Llandrindod Wells to Harlech on a non-school weekday in September 1980, I was in the best place. In addition, there was a file detailing all the conferences, exhibitions and courses on the history of the bus, from the omnibuses of the early 20th century to the hoppa buses of the present day. On the front cover of the file was a photograph of Geraint holding a cup having won the quiz held on the last day of a bus enthusiasts' conference held in Wakefield in 1995, his specialist subject being Different Types Of Fuel Used In Buses Operated By The Ilkeston And District Traction Company, 1927 To The Present.
"Anyway," Geraint said as he led me back into the drawing-room, "It is part of my mission now to get myself more involved with the community as a whole, so having heard more about it I will be delighted to lend my singing voice to your group and look forward to joining you."
Although it's good to have him, I can't say his recruitment to the ranks is the greatest moment in the short history of the Lambsball Green Singers. And in some ways I'd almost rather not have him with us at all than the worry about the prospect of having to rearrange a pre-booked event on being informed that it clashes with anything from a pre-war double decker rally on the seafront at Weymouth to an exhibition to mark the 25th anniversary of the first deployment of the British Leyland C6100 for the Saturday shoppers' park-and-ride service in Worksop.

Monday 28th April

To Dellford Music Supplies at lunchtime. I'd been looking forward to a good browse in their collection of vocal music and had a number of titles of collections which Alan had suggested. No sooner had I entered the shop, however, than I was pounced upon by a short fierce-looking woman I assumed to be the owner and asked what I wanted. I felt like a house burglar caught redhanded by the occupants.

"I wonder if you have these titles," I said, giving her Alan's suggested list. She snatched it from my hand and summarily announced with barely a glance at its contents that none of them were in stock.

I asked if they could be ordered. "Well, I'll have to check the computer, won't I," she said, as though I was in some way to blame. In the time it took her to log on and attempt to key in the relevant information I dare say I could probably have travelled to the wholesalers and simply picked up the copies from there. In due course, however, she deigned to volunteer the information that the earliest I could expect to receive any of it was in about four weeks' time.

"That is, if they've called off the leather-tanners' overtime ban in Botswana," I said in an attempt to humour her. But I might as well have been trying to humour a tub of overripe cottage cheese. So over we went to plan B, namely see what other music they had which was usable by my new group. In response to which she snatched a set of keys from the cash desk and led me to the top drawer of a stout metal filing cabinet which appeared to have been triple locked. It would have been easier to break into MI5 headquarters and I was only surprised I wasn't asked to complete an application form in quadruplicate, produce my birth certificate and passport, and don protective gloves and face mask. Under rigorous surveillance, I was permitted to peruse a list of contents of the drawer, announce my choice and allow the store manager to remove the selected items for me to consider in more detail; in the absence of a pair of tweezers, to have asked to handle it myself would have been like rolling up my trouser leg in the presence of a Rottweiler and asking him how he was enjoying his six-month diet of organic courgettes.

Ten minutes later, the contents of metal drawer once more safe from fire, flood or pre-emptive nuclear strike, I was on my way back to work, reflecting that by my purchase of two items from the aforementioned container I had at least ensured retention of all my faculties in one piece. But how well the *a cappella* arrangements by Percy Landseer-Scott B.Mus(1900-1977) of *I've Got A Loverly Bunch Of Coconuts* and *The Marrow Song (I've Never Seen One As Big As That Before)* will go down at Phyllis Aughterlonie's garden soiree is another matter altogether.

MAY

Thursday 1st May

Our first rehearsal began very well, using some music Alan had unearthed and kindly copied for us. He conducted, and his wife Debbie kindly came along and accompanied on a miniature keyboard. We'd prefer a piano, especially for works which need piano or organ accompaniment, and I've told Stan I'm on the lookout for one. But despite the lack of piano,we sang confidently and competently, and have already agreed a draft programme for our entertainments next month, starting with the 7th June which has been confirmed as the date for our church concert in aid of the Samaritans. I felt elated and excited that from such unpromising beginnings I'd formed a very skilled and accomplished music group.

Then Greg Corbally turned up.

Things started to go downhill immediately I saw those placed either side of him moving a couple of paces away from him, leaving him in not-so-splendid isolation. Although he had discarded his ghastly silver puffa jacket, for tonight at any rate, his state of personal hygiene was no better and his voice was if anything even worse. From time to time, when one of his more insensitive pieces of tuning had a particularly adverse effect on the piece we happened to be singing, I detected a wince from Alan and a look of utter despair on the faces of Jack and Mike. I didn't dare look at the girls, as one glance in their direction after Mr C had opened his mouth for the first time suggested they would not so much prefer to be three chair widths away from him as on a different continent altogether.

I'd planned to sing till nine thirty and give Greg a voice test which I hoped would give us some pretext to get rid of him there and then, but by ten past nine I'd had enough and called a halt. I certainly wasn't aiming for perfection in my group: I'm happy to include as many people as are keen to join us, and tailor our standards and expectations accordingly, but there must be limits. I was determined that I would take Mr C aside and call upon every last fragment of my assertiveness skills to tell him that, notwithstanding my wish to involve the local community in the group, he was no longer welcome. But before I could begin, he himself came up to me and announced "I just can't tell you how much I enjoyed that. I've had an awful week. If I hadn't had this tonight, I'm not sure I'd have had the strength to carry on any more." And that was just the start. Eventually I was persuaded to defer passing judgement and adjourn the proceedings pending a full psychiatric assessment and a pre-hearing review at the next rehearsal. So much for assertiveness.

While I was hearing about how I'd reduced the week's suicide statistics by one, all the others save Alan and Debbie had left with alarming rapidity. And sure enough, as the door had closed on the last one to go,

Alan walked slowly up to me and said "Hate to say this, but all the others have made it clear that unless Greg goes, they will."
There it is then. Our new group only two hours old and already I have a mass walkout on my hands. True, I have experienced it once before. But I suspect the impact this time will be rather greater than that on the Wolverhampton Polytechnic Glee Club when a third of its membership left a rehearsal in protest at being asked to sing a Liverpool Medley dressed in curly wigs and pink shellsuits.

Sunday 4th May

At church this morning Geraint asked us to make a point of going up to a visitor after the service, welcome them and find out more about them. I was sitting next to a pleasant-looking woman attired in a striking yellow and black striped dress and it seemed natural to introduce myself to her. Unfortunately, apart from volunteering the fact that her name was Margaret, she was disappointingly monosyllabic in her responses, so after a few moments' interrogation I excused myself and targeted a tall smartly dressed man two pews back whom I'd certainly never met before. "I take it you're a visitor here?" I said to him.
"No, not really," he said. "I've lived in the village for twenty years and have attended this service most Sundays for the last twelve."
It would have been all too easy to have slunk away in abject embarrassment, something at which I've become remarkably proficient since joining this church, but the genial way in which he responded to my question suggested it was at least worth my while asking him his name, for my benefit if not for his. He told me he was Duncan Adams, a solicitor in private practice, dividing his time between his offices in Dellford and the City. I told him about my new group and he replied he might be persuaded to come and join us, other commitments permitting.
Before allowing my hopes to be raised up too high, though, I felt compelled to warn him that because of one particular individual I was having serious doubts about the future of the whole project.
"Not Greg Corbally, is it?" Duncan asked.
I admitted that it was. "I was just about to sack him," I said, "and he told me he was thinking of ending it all. I had no choice."
"Oh, he'll never give you a choice," Duncan grinned. "They've been trying for years to get him out of the choral society. Emergency committee meetings sitting on till half past midnight, sometimes, working out how to do it. But every time they pluck up the courage, he produces some new heart-rending excuse for his incompetence. He lost his parents many years back and his brother doesn't speak to him. So he's fallen back on his menagerie. Two years ago it was his cat who'd died. Last year it was his dog. And six months ago his canary. They were thinking of

calling in the RSPCA at one stage. Wondering what he was doing to the wretched creatures."
"How many pets does he actually own?" I asked. "If he lives on his own in a flat, he can't have that many, surely."
"Oh, can't he," said Duncan. "According to reliable sources, he's also the proud owner of two budgies, a parrot, a hamster, a guinea pig, two goldfish and two rabbits. Soon to become six."
That's an awful lot of late night emergency committee meetings.

Tuesday 6th May

Katie suggested we had a weekend away and, recalling a superb music shop in York with a rather more conciliatory policy towards customers than Dellford Music Supplies, we've arranged a long weekend in Yorkshire.
It was our second rehearsal tonight and I was absolutely dreading the thought of having to do Greg's voice test and tell him he was no good. Although not given to private prayer during working hours, I have to say that I prayed harder than I had ever prayed for him to ring me and say he couldn't come tonight. Although there was no phone call, miraculously, wondrously, he did not in fact turn up. Joined by Duncan from Sunday on bass, and also Geraint who sportingly joined Alan on alto, we had a superb evening's singing, perfecting the pieces we'd done last week and polishing up our loverly bunch of coconuts as if it was going out of fashion. I felt almost tearful with elation and pride. Yes, I want more singers, but while we're just the select bunch that we are, it's great to make such a good crisp and disciplined sound. We actually went on far later than I'd intended, and it wasn't until ten past ten that we finally finished. Stan, who'd come in at nine thirty to lock up, took it all in good part. He mentioned that there's a piano going begging, shut away in the old scout building at the east end of the village, and has offered to meet me on Thursday night to look at it and, if we like it, help me move it to the Assembly Room.
As we were leaving, he enquired if Greg Corbally had turned up tonight.
"No, thank God," I said. "Literally, thank God. I'm completely overcome. I prayed so hard for him not to come, and amazingly he didn't."
"Not so amazingly," grinned Stan. "I rang him this afternoon. Told him the rehearsal was tomorrow."

Thursday 8th May

Stan and I had agreed six thirty at the old scout building, reached by following a twisting, pot-holed track. When I got there I wasn't too impressed. The whole place had a real air of neglect about it, with graffiti plastered on the walls, all the windows smashed down one side, and

teenagers kicking a football around on the concreted area outside the front of the building. Although the wooden front door was locked, one of the boys helpfully escorted me round to a side door which was wide open. I didn't like to ask why or how.
I made my way into the main hall, empty save for a few rusty chairs, a card table stacked with plates and wine glasses, and a bicycle wheel. There was no sign of any piano but I noticed a flight of steps going up one side of the hall with a door at the top. At that moment my mobile phone rang. It was Stan.
"Really sorry, Dave," he said. "I'm running late. I've just had Edna Mudge yelling down the phone at me because the rehearsal overran the other night. She said we only had the hall till half past nine. Never mind nobody else wanted it. Never mind that she hasn't gone in there after six o'clock since 1923. Only just got rid of her."
"It won't take you long to get down here, though, will it?" I enquired.
"Longer than you think," said Stan. "I'd just got into the bath when she rang. I'm sitting in it now."
"Well, where is the piano?" I asked. "I can at least look at it."
"It's in the cupboard at the top of the stairs," said Stan. "But I wouldn't….."
At that moment there was a deafening bang, doubtless caused by one of the budding Wayne Rooneys outside crashing the ball against the front wall, followed by a gale of hysterical laughter. Impulsively I walked round to remonstrate with them and immediately the laughter gave way to jeers and various obscenity-filled remarks questioning both my IQ and my parentage. I returned whence I came and resumed my call. "You were saying?" I said to Stan.
"I was just saying that I really wouldn't….."
There was another loud crash followed by a further verbal salvo which to the slightly hard of hearing might have seemed like references to my skills at plucking, flossing and banking, and then a further smash which sounded more like a bottle than a football. In the absence of a police community beat officer, a representative from the Dellford And District Child And Adolescent Community Mental Health Support And Advice Service, or a sub-machine gun, I decided it was best to ignore it and once again spoke into the phone – just in time to hear Stan say "See you in twenty minutes. Cheers." The line then went dead. And further attempts to call him back proved unsuccessful.
I didn't exactly relish the prospect of a twenty-minute wait in this dump, but thankfully the banging seemed to stop and a cautious look outside confirmed that the village's aspiring ASBO owners had gone, for the moment at least. To pass the time, I walked up the little flight of stairs

and gave a token tug at the door, more in hope than expectation of getting into the piano cupboard, and resigned to it being locked.
The result was dramatic. The door flew open – the handle coming away in my hand – and I involuntarily leapt sideways as the piano, as if desperate for freedom and fresh air following its enforced restraint, shot out of the cupboard and tumbled down the stairs. With its castors working overtime, it careered across the floor towards the card table, and with contemptuous ease it swept it aside, throwing the table across the room and the plates and wine glasses to the ground in a succession of earsplitting smashes. Rapidly quitting the scene of the accident without stopping to give details, the piano headed confidently for the front door where I assumed its progress would be halted, but the piano had other ideas; gaining speed, it crashed straight through the flimsy wood panels and out into the open air onto the sloping concrete forecourt. Now hot on its trail, I followed it out through the hole it had created, just in time to see it wobble unsteadily and, after a tantalising pause, spin off the forecourt and disappear with a loud splash into the adjoining ditch.
I stood there helplessly, hardly able to believe what had just happened. Mercifully, Stan arrived very shortly afterwards and, not trusting myself to speak, I pointed down at the last resting place of the ill-fated instrument, one castor of which could be seen tentatively poking from the muddy, reedy depths.
"You got it out of the cupboard all right then," said Stan simply.
I confirmed I had. At a cost of a handle, a card table, a dozen china plates, eight wine glasses, a wooden door and the hire of a firm of specialist ditch dredgers.
"Oh, don't worry," said Stan airily. "They're bound to blame it on the kids. It was probably them that set the piano up to do that anyway. I did try and warn you not to touch anything but there was a problem with your mobile. Never mind. "
"But.....but.... what about the piano?" I spluttered
"It's all right," said Stan. "Couldn't play it even if you wanted to. No key to get into it."
"But I thought you told me you had it," I said.
Without a word Stan put his hand in his trouser pocket, withdrew a small object and, bringing to bear all the skills that had made him Dellford Cricket Club's best bowler during their record-breaking 1970 and 1971 seasons, hurled it high into the air and watched it dive down into the impenetrable gorse bushes on the fringes of the Dellford municipal sewage works.
"Not any more," he said.

Wednesday 14th May

Well, now we know. The subject of Friday night's Lambsball Green Dippers quiz evening is Michael Fish. Since the only thing I, and probably 99 per cent of sane individuals, know and indeed wish to know about him is that he wrongly said there would be no hurricane, I think that when the quiz starts I will take a back seat. In a coach bound for Stranraer.

I spent most of today, as I'd spent much of my weekend up North, going over and over in my mind what to say to Greg at tonight's rehearsal. I'd already had to ring him to apologise for his turning up on the wrong night last week, so even before tonight's confrontation I hardly felt I had the forces of right on my side. Anyway, he duly came along tonight; he was late, meaning I couldn't voice-test him first thing and get rid of him, and he proceeded to ruin all the pieces I'd brought back from York and that we covered in the first half. Charlie Tompkins happened to be there and one glimpse of his facial expression made it crystal clear to me what he thought of the sound we were making. I decided I couldn't leave it any longer than the interval so popped to the loo for a final rehearsal of what I was going to say, then, almost trembling with apprehension, I asked to speak to Greg alone.

"I'm really terribly sorry, Greg," I said to him. "I've been really bowled over by your enthusiasm and commitment to this group. It's part of my wish to create something for the whole community to be involved in, and I am so so loath to turn away anybody who is anxious to join. I know we'd arranged to do a voice test this evening. But I've heard enough from you already and I have to say that I just don't feel you're quite right for us just now. There are a number of concerns and issues which other members have with you which I am happy to go into if you need me to, but I'm sure I don't need to tell you what those are. I appreciate you have a lot of difficulties in your personal life but there are organisations in and around Dellford that can help you and build up your confidence in a way that's better for you in the longer term than singing with us. Now. Is there anything you'd like to say?"

I braced myself for a flood of tears, a fit of rage or news of the latest mystery virus to have sent one or more of his pet cagebirds crashing from their perches…..but remarkably, no such outburst ensued.

"No, no, that's fine," was his unexpected reply. "Thank you for having me. I'll go now."

And he did.

I suddenly felt a huge wave of relief and also enormous satisfaction that I'd handled the matter so assertively and yet so discreetly. Morale soared, and for the rest of the evening we sang better than we'd ever sung before.

We all went to the Welldiggers after the practice. As we stood at the bar waiting to order, Jack turned to me and said "I think you owe Charlie one."
"Why?" I asked.
"Well, he was the one who got rid of you know who."
"I don't understand," I said. "I spoke to him during the interval."
"Yes," said Jack. "But that was after Charlie went up to him and told him that he knew of heaps of rancid horse manure that sang better than he did. And smelt better too."

Friday 16th May

The Dippers' Quiz Night at the Welldiggers. I really was in two minds about whether to go, but decided that I needed more voices for the group so went along in the hope that I could obtain some recruits and still keep a reasonably low profile. As Katie said, "Most of the sane ones are likely to be in the background anyway."
On arrival, I was directed to the Wellies Bar, in which there was certainly quite a good crowd, mostly male and in their thirties or early forties. In the middle of them I recognised at least two of the New Year's Day crowd, poring over pieces of paper and obviously preparing themselves for the quiz to come, but fortunately they either didn't see or didn't recognise me. I got myself a drink and sat down a fair distance away from them, next to a man and a woman who I took to be in their early thirties and who at least looked reasonably normal. They introduced themselves to me as Mark and Susan, and told me they had moved into the village only a fortnight ago. They said they'd heard about the Dippers and decided to come along out of curiosity. I asked them if they sang, and they told me no, but they'd love to have a go, and, better still, they had made friends with another couple in the village who they were confident would be interested as well. Minutes later, I was arranging for them all to join us at the Assembly Room next week for a voice test. A result.
With the quiz being announced as starting any second now, I decided it was time to make a quick getaway. Joyfully, I leapt from my seat, thrust open the door of the bar – and collided head-on with a young man carrying a tray laden with plates of food. Within moments the floor was a seething mass of steak and kidney pie, beef Wellington, salmon fishcakes and Yorksire ham with pineapple, this rapidly congealing mixture accompanied by an eclectic medley of farm fresh cauliflower, succulent baby carrots drizzled with lemon on a bed of rice, chunky hand-cooked chips, luscious cheese and Moselle sauce, rich onion gravy, refreshing raspberry jus, and delicately shaved parmesan. Plus fragments of indiscriminately tossed dinner plate.

There was a pregnant silence and then the whole place erupted into laughter and cheers. Seconds later, as the UN were summoned to provide emergency support to clear the devastation and the news channels throughout the country began broadcasting disaster helplines for those wishing to enquire about the fate of loved ones and make donations to relief agencies, I found myself being gathered up by the New Year's Day crowd, offered further alcoholic refreshment and told that once the remaining pieces of delicately shaved pineapple and farm fresh fishcakes had been scraped from the knee area of my trousers, I was needed to make up the numbers for the Rock Salmons. By now devoid of any capacity for logical thought, I found myself on the team.
The next hour saw more information being exchanged about Michael Fish than most rational people could take in a lifetime, from his collection of over 100 Fish motif ties to the punk record by Rachel and Nicki – whoever they were – dedicated to him in 1985 . Thankfully, being in a team, I was never called upon to expose my almost complete ignorance about the man. Until, to my horror, it was announced that following the last round, the scores between the two teams were level and there was to be a sudden death play-off, head-to-head between one representative for each team, each nominated by the respective opposition. It was no surprise whatsoever to be nominated and to find myself standing before the assembled company against a completely bald and very short man with a strong Lancashire accent, sporting a salmon-pink coloured shirt, a bow tie covered in shark fin patterns, and long baggy shorts with the logo "Just when you thought it was safe to go back in the water." I didn't know whether I felt sorrier for him or me.
"The question, then," said the quiz master. "Whoever answers correctly first wins. What is Michael Fish's wife's name?"
Remembering the woman I'd got to join us earlier, I made a pure guess. "Susan?" I enquired tentatively.
"CORRECT!" yelled the quiz master. Suddenly there was a deafening roar of cheers and I found myself mobbed by all the other nine members of the Rock Salmon team, elevated from fish cake destroyer to hero of the hour. Anyone would think I had scored the winning goal in the World Cup Final.
As the cheers died down, the quiz master stood up again. "As you know, we make one promotion to Second Dipper at each May Quiz night," he said. "And who better to receive the award, and the Dippy Parcel, than our quiz champ – David Braithwaite!!"
More cheers came my way, as did a brown paper parcel which I was instructed required opening forthwith. I tore it open to uncover a pair of swimming trunks of pink and yellow so loud that I perceived a serious possibility of breach of maximum permitted decibel levels. "And now,"

said the quiz master. "while our new Second Dipper elect gets his trunks on in readiness for his initation, I….."
The word "initiation" was enough. Hideously aware of an impending date with the well in the pub garden, and its multifarious contents to boot, I muttered something about an even more urgent appointment with a comfortable armchair and the late film, got up and positively hurtled exit-wards, wholly indifferent to what damage I did to anything that stood in my way. No matter whether it was a bulk consignment of deep-frozen caviar shipped in from the Hotel Grande in Monte Carlo or Mr Fish himself making a surprise guest appearance wearing a gold-painted crocodile-skin catsuit.

Sunday 18th May
Our concert on June 7th got a good plug from the vicar in church this morning. During the notices he advised that in the absence of Mrs Dublin, "tickets are available afterwards from Lotta Spondon and Joan Board W….I mean, Joan Ward Banks." The hideous consequences of his not stopping himself in time weren't lost on me, and knowing I needed to speak to her afterwards, thought of little else for the rest of the service. "Ward Banks, Ward Banks, Ward Banks," I said to myself severely as I went up for communion. "Ward Banks, Ward Banks," I muttered as we filed out afterwards.
I felt the least I could do was to introduce myself to the ticket sellers and extended my hand to the first. "Joan Ward Banks?" I said, carefully. She smiled and nodded.
I'd done it. Beaming with relief, I turned to her colleague and, shaking her hand warmly, announced "So you must be Lotta Condom."
Following the piano disaster of ten days ago, we'd decided to advertise for a piano in the *Chronicle* and the ad which appeared in last Thursday's edition had yielded three responses. Alan, Debbie and I decided to follow them up this afternoon. Despite repeatedly ringing the doorbell of the homeowner offering us the first instrument, there was no answer. The second was pronounced by Debbie to be absolutely ideal, in excellent condition and recently tuned, and we would assuredly have agreed to take it had the owner not insisted on a non-negotiable price which could have only been afforded by the group after a lottery win or a trip to the bank with a balaclava and imitation firearm. And as for the third, that was certainly eminently affordable but unfortunately possessed a couple of features that proved to be deal-breakers. Namely, a missing middle C key – with MIND THE GAP and arrow helpfully written in indelible ink on the adjacent B natural key – and, whenever any keys in the octave above middle C were depressed, a muffled sound suggesting that their insides had been coated with a family-size portion of Wrigley's Spearmint.

Monday 19th May

A very apologetic call at lunchtime from the owner of the first house we'd tried yesterday. I popped round and was offered a brand new keyboard, still in its wrapping, which I was assured sounded just like a piano. And apparently, according to the wording on the wrapping TEN TOP INTERNATIONAL PIANISTS DEFY YOU TO TELL THE DIFFERENCE. The owner had won it in a raffle but said she was completely unmusical and was only too pleased to give it to a good home. I was certainly pleased to be able to relieve her of it, at a very good price indeed.

However, Alan, Debbie and I were not so pleased to get the box over to the Assembly Room this evening, unpack the various components and discover that to assemble the base of the unit successfully required both a Masters degree from the South Carolina Institute Of Applied Science and the engagement of a reputable conjurer among whose skills was the ability to produce screws and nuts from thin air.

Eventually we found ourselves with a unit that looked secure enough and switched it on. To our delight, it seemed to work, and announced its obvious pleasure to have found a new and happy home by belting out a very piano-like rendition of *The Entertainer*. Not content with that, it gave a repeat performance. And another. And another. Until we all began to feel horribly like one does when one's phone call is in a queue and one finds oneself listening to the same piece of music over and over again. And unfortunately, not one of the many buttons and keys on the unit was able to prevent the crowning work of S. Joplin Esq. continuing to assailing our eardrums. I looked again at the buttons, and in a flash of inspiration selected one labelled MEMORY and one labelled DELETE, and hit them both together. The effect was instant. The pressure of my two forefingers caused the base to wobble and then crumple, sending the keyboard descending to the floor with a smash which generated an avalanche of cacophonous sounds that even Stockhausen in his prime would have dismissed as overly adventurous. Then a blissful silence.

"At least you got rid of the frigging Entertainer," said Alan.

Despite it being nearly six thirty, a phone call revealed that the Dellford Piano Doctor was open for evening surgery and we duly conveyed the lifeless remains to his reception area without further delay. After conducting a brief examination, he regrettably pronounced the patient to be dead on arrival and beyond any hope of resuscitation but having offered us his sincere condolences he offered either to dispose of the body in a humane fashion or, with our consent, donate it for the purpose of future scientific research.

Seemed to spend the whole of the rest of the evening on the phone; firstly the committee to remind them of our meeting on Wednesday night, then

the secretary of the Happy Harmonists who said she would be "delighted" for me to join them at a rehearsal when they resumed in June after a break, and thirdly Margaret Donaldson, the secretary of the Dellford Operatic Society, who told me that rehearsals for *The Mikado* are now well under way and I am "most welcome" to come along next Tuesday night. Apparently there is one principal part which is as yet uncast.
"To be honest," I said, "I'm not really wanting to be in it. As I explained, I want to see if there are any Lambsball Green residents in the group. You told me you couldn't divulge that over the phone."
"Yes, of course," Mrs Donaldson cooed, "but I have to say that there are real worries among our committee regarding membership levels. We've never known a principal part to remain unfilled so late in a production. And the male chorus is especially thin. We really could do with you on board."
"I'd love to help," I said, "but, as I say, it's not why I'm ringing. I simply want to come and observe."
"I know," said Mrs Donaldson. "We've lost, I don't know, a good seven members in the last two years. Jim McTaggart with his heart, Bob Eldridge with his leg, Rose Warwick with her veins....it's desperate. Can you stay on after Tuesday's rehearsal to audition?"
I didn't know whether to reach for my hankie or my gun. "I'm sorry, I don't want to audition," I said. "Look, I think it's best I just don't come on Tuesday after all."
"Oh, no, we'd like to have you," said Mrs Donaldson. "If the part we've in mind is too high or low for you, we can probably rejig. Ellis Thomas is very good about swapping round. He did Little Buttercup for us last year when we were stuck. And Cameron Smalley's got a most useful top A flat...."
Naturally I was pleased for Cameron Smalley, but at that moment I felt as I had done years ago in a drama production when we found the dialogue going round in circles with no obvious means of escape. And almost wishing that rather than talking to Mrs Donaldson from the comfort of my armchair, I was in fact on stage in the icy cold South Glenton community hall fighting my way through *They Came From Mars And Landed Outside The Farndale Avenue Church Hall In Time For The Townswomen's Guild Coffee Morning.*

Wednesday 21st May
Received a call from the Piano Doctor this afternoon saying he had a decent-sized keyboard of his own that he no longer had any use for, and he was kind enough to deliver it to us at the Assembly Room tonight just in time for the voice tests which were to precede our committee meeting.

Better still, now we have a proper keyboard, Debbie has agreed to become our official accompanist.
We had no less than four prospective members to test: Duncan Adams whom I'd met in church earlier this month, Mark and Susan from the other night, and a friend of Susan's named Gail who like me works in Dellford and moved here just before Christmas. All of them were fine. and I was delighted immediately afterwards to report the fact to the committee – less Perfrement, delayed by an overrunning meeting of the Business Efficiency Sub Committee.
"Still not a choir as such, is it," sniffed Charlie. "I mean, it's still barely double figures, and that's including the vicar on non bus-worshipping days."
I felt like asking him how many of those he'd recruited, but for fear of being held in contempt and consigned to two hours' detention in the detergent cabinet, I merely said "I know. But we've two events lined up next month. Shows we're developing."
"It shows you've formed a close harmony group," said Charlie. "But punters can only take so many of these part songs, you know, doo-be-doo, biddly bong, tiddley pom, tickety boo, gottle o'geer, roly poly, gammon and spinach, and Lord knows what else. Or madrigals. All that falala-ing and awful Elizabethan doggerel – Lusty Dick Firkin dancing on his jerkin, and that nonsense. You need to be thinking a lot bigger."
His argument was unanswerable and my spirits, so high just twenty minutes previously, had now plummeted through the floor into the basement and were now heading inexorably for a small farming community in Southern Queensland.
"I am doing my best," I said. "I'm continuing to scout for members in the Dellford Operatic and the Happy Harmonists."
"Operatic? You must be mad," Charlie snorted. "Everyone just sings the tune. Apparently one year a new chorusmaster asked them if there were any tenors, and half of them started going through their wallets. As for the Happy Harmonists, if they went on the *X Factor* they'd be laughed off the stage before they'd opened their mouths."
"Well, what about an *X Factor*?" the Spadger piped up. "Lambsball Green's very own talent contest. People come along, do their turn, prizes, food, loads of undiscovered talent. It's been done before. Well, similar anyway, in 1985. In fact, I…."
"Yes, thank you, Angus," Alan put in. "What about the judging? Who'd do that?"
"I'll tell you," said Flora, pointing to Charlie. "If he's judging, I'm out."
"My dear Francesca," said Charlie, "If I were asked you can be sure I'd apply to each candidate the same principles that have governed my long years on the Bench."

"That's exactly what I'm afraid of," said Flora.
"Well, I think it's absurd anyway," said Charlie. "I don't want to give up a precious free evening listening to a queue of Frank Spencer impersonators and Gladys at number 18 murdering Little Polly Flinders."
"There's no guarantee it'll get us anyone new," said Alan, "and it's a lot of work."
"I have concerns that wholly inappropriate comments made by judges will be offensive to the competitors and we will find ourselves with issues around that," said Flora.
"If as much as one chair leg is out of place at the end of the evening, Edna Mudge will be along with her Tesco carrier bag of assorted Molotov cocktails," warned Stan.
We all agreed the whole idea was a complete non starter. Which of course is why 30 minutes later we'd agreed a firm date for it, with responsibility for all aspects, from advertising to refreshments, from judges to prizes, from crowd control to drying the eyes of unsuccessful competitors, squarely on my shoulders. I think I'd rather have been forced to spend an evening supping gammon and spinach with Lusty Dick Firkin.

Tuesday 27th May

After a lovely Bank Holiday weekend with Katie's parents, felt in a good relaxed frame of mind as I made my way to the Boys Brigade Hall in Dellford for the operatic rehearsal which was due to begin at 7.45. Apparently rehearsals were changed from a 7.30 to a 7.45 start because most people arrived at or around 7.40. Which of course now meant that most people arrived at around 7.55. We actually didn't get going till nearly ten past eight, and for the next hour concentrated on music, the early middle-aged conductor helping us to note-bash our way through the Act 1 finale. There were about twenty women; although there was a very attractive girl playing the part of Pitti-Sing, most of them were well into their sixties and beyond. As far as men were concerned, there were just eight, three of whom obviously had solo parts. The remaining five were evidently contented just to sing the soprano line an octave lower, reverting to a tentative attempt at the tenor or bass part when bidden by the long-suffering conductor, and then, when the whole chorus was asked to sing, going back to the soprano line an octave lower once more. I noticed that when there was a solo line for Yum-Yum, the teenage heroine of the piece, it was sung by a white-haired lady of about 70, with a wobble that reminded me of our celebrated blue jellies served up to us by Mrs Watkins at Lower Nuthaven Road Primary, and a high note so screechy that I was sure I heard an owl just outside the window answering her call and thinking this was his lucky night.
"Good of her to fill in, anyway," I said to the man on my left.

"Fill in?" he echoed. "That's the part she's doing."
We somehow managed to get through not only the Act 1 finale but the chorus music for Act 2 as well, before stopping at the civilised time of 9.25 and being invited to partake of light refreshments in the adjoining room.
"Cakes tonight," my earlier singing companion informed me, licking his lips. "Cindy Bailey's been working at the bakery today. So we get the leftovers." And get we certainly did, in the form of a rich assortment of doughnuts, cream slices and sugary Bath buns. Having been on the point of giving up and going home just minutes before, I suddenly felt a significant upsurge in morale. Indeed, after enjoying the moistest jammiest doughnut I had ever eaten, I was, geriatric juvenile leads apart, beginning to get quite keen on this society; even more so when my companion, in answer to my enquiry about Lambsball Green residents in the society, said "There's one member, Lucy Boustead, the one who's playing Pitti-Sing."
"Great, thanks," I said. " I'll go and talk to her now."
"Well, actually….."
He got no further, for at that very moment we were asked to take our seats for notices. The first six or seven were quite straightforward, but we hit the buffers somewhat when we moved on to the arrangements for the summer barbecue at Raymond and Irene's, and who was to bring what. By the time it had been agreed that Leonard would provide the garden chairs, Rosemary would supply the briquettes, and, following a heated debate, that a change to rule 16.1.8 to permit the society to increase its subsidy for the cost of the food and drink from 25 to 28 per cent would be thrashed out at an extraordinary general meeting three weeks on Wednesday, it was nearly ten o'clock and I was expecting us all to be released. I could not have been more wrong; at an hour when most right-thinking people would be curled up on their settee with a mug of Horlicks and being told by the *Crimewatch* presenters to sleep well and not to have nightmares, seemingly from nowhere a short plump stern-faced woman in her fifties, dressed in a light grey jogging suit and holding a referee's whistle, commanded us to rise from our posteriors (that being a polite translation of what was actually said) in order to commence some "serious blocking" on Act 1. I had hoped to get to see Lucy but any hope of that was snuffed out when the girls and the men were summarily separated, the girls to look at the "Schoolgirls we eighteen and under" chorus – which one guessed needed some sort of disclaimer to prevent proceedings under the Trades Descriptions Act – and the men to go into a back room to revise moves for the opening chorus which, our jogging-suited producer charitably announced, "reminded me last week of a troupe of drunken carthorses on a works outing to Cleethorpes." Like a

helpless sea bather caught in a receding tide, I found myself being sucked inexorably onto the dance floor and working for the next 25 minutes with a somewhat ineffectual assistant producer to look again at the sequence of moves that had been learnt during the previous session. We were then joined by a woman who had been sitting in front of me during the earlier music rehearsal and who proceeded to suggest we did it all completely differently, devoting the next 40 minutes to a sequence of wholly new moves. I was at something of an advantage, having nothing from the previous week to unlearn, but as I'd been blessed from birth with a splendid pair of left feet my progress round the floor could most aptly be described as tentative. Finally, at ten minutes past eleven, we were summoned back and invited to share the fruits of our labours with The Jogging Suit. We weren't really on track from the start and it was no surprise to be derailed after a paltry sixteen bars with a peremptory blast of her instrument and curtly informed that not only did we resemble even more inebriated beasts of burden than heretofore, but our offering ran entirely contrary to how she'd instructed it to be choreographed. She then announced that she herself would replot it with us on…..Sunday week.

Happening to be standing beside my companion from earlier, whose appetite for Cindy Bailey's calorific coffee-time treats was evidenced both by the size of his stomach and the traces of synthetic cream decorating the lower reaches of his moustache, I asked "What does she mean, Sunday week?"

"We'll be rehearsing all day on Sundays from 8th June for five weeks," he explained. "Ten till six."

Although the horror at the prospect of this was slightly mitigated by the welcome tidings that we were calling it a night, and I was thus free to seek out Lucy, my relief was short-lived. The producer, looking straight in my direction, called for hush again and announced "Now I have some good news. As you may be aware just before tonight's rehearsal we held an emergency committee meeting to decide whether we could proceed with the show at all, lacking as you know a man to play the leading tenor part, Nanki-Poo. We were going to ask our new member, David Braithwaite, to formally audition, but I think on the strength of what we've heard from him tonight that he will fit the bill admirably and enable the show to continue. So, David, will you play the part for us and enable the show to go ahead?"

Aware that at that stage it would have needed less bottle to rip up an IOU presented by the Incredible Hulk, I took the easy way out, forcing a sickly smile and giving a submissive nod. For the second time in less than a fortnight I was feted as the hero of the hour. Ten minutes later I had not only parted with the cost of a year's subscription and a month's tea and doughnut money, but had committed myself to, among other things, a

photo shoot for the local press in Escott Park at 7.30am a fortnight on Saturday, a 30-minute visit with the other soloists to the St Cuthbert's Twilight Home in Calthrop Road four weeks on Friday, and, seven days after that, a soloists' weekend music and movement skills workshop in a disused carpet warehouse just outside Daventry.
And I still hadn't spoken to Lucy Boustead, who had disappeared. As I emerged from the hall I found myself walking beside my sweet-toothed companion and asked him where I might locate her. "Probably where I'm going now, in the pub," he said. "Care to join us?"
"If she's there, yes," I said. "You were about to say earlier she lives in Lambsball Green?"
"No," he replied. "I was going to tell you earlier. Her brother does."
"And does he sing?" I asked weakly, clinging to the last remaining straw with the zealous determination of a Ribena addict.
"I doubt it," he replied. "There aren't many amateur operatic societies on North Sea oil rigs."

Wednesday 28th May
Spent a largely sleepless night thinking how I might get myself out of this unwanted new commitment. The urgency was redoubled when, after barely having had a chance to sit down at my desk this morning, I received, hand-delivered, a schedule of rehearsals for the show week in September, running from Tuesday 16th to Saturday 20th. This is preceded by rehearsals every night of the previous week except Saturday, then a full day on Sunday including band call and "first dress rehearsal, full costume, no make-up" commencing at 9am and lasting "all day into the evening."
Maddeningly, Mrs Donaldson was unavailable all day, and I then had a rehearsal for our Saturday week concert tonight. After an excellent evening's work, we finished in good time so rather than go to the pub I came straight home and thankfully this time did get through to the hitherto elusive operatic society secretary.
"Mrs Donaldson?" I said. "David Braithwaite. Now, I'm…."
"Aha!" she exclaimed. "Our new wandering minstrel. I cannot tell you how thrilled we are. I was at a lunch today with the mayor and the leader of the borough council, and was describing you as our saviour. You've made all the difference between doing the show and not doing it. A vital event in our social and cultural calendar. This is huge for the town, you know."
"There is just one problem," I said, feeling suddenly less like a graduate of the Harvard School Of Interpersonal And Communication Skills than a half-cooked semolina pudding in a thunderstorm. "It's the time factor."

"Oh, yes," said Mrs Donaldson. "You got your rehearsal schedule today, I hope. Now, I know you'll have found it alarming, but let me straight away give you some reassurance."
That sounded at least moderately hopeful. Perhaps I was to be excused some of the sessions. "In what way?" I enquired.
"Well," she went on, "you'll have noticed the absence of a technical rehearsal on the schedule. That was inadvertently omitted. It's on the Saturday before, starting at 9am, finishing when we finish, but do be prepared for it to go on."
"And then back the next day straight after breakfast," I said. With heavy irony, I went on "Sleeping bags provided, I suppose."
"We'll have one there for you," said Mrs Donaldson. "And do you like your breakfast eggs boiled or scrambled?"

JUNE

Sunday 1st June

Felt it was only right to try and help move some tickets for Saturday, as I'm told they aren't going at all well, despite the best efforts of Joan and Lotta. The vicar did an excellent plug for it during the notices, adding "I'm going to be singing in it myself – I hope that doesn't put too many of you off." Unfortunately from the response I got afterwards, it seemed his hopes were in vain. Connie Farrant had booked up for Grease, although whether she meant the stage show, the film or a meal at Stan's Caf in Heavitree Road remained unstated; Audrey Kibble White announced "I'm going in for my bunions" – careless of her to have left them behind; Anthea Parsons was "having the children" – judging by her size I couldn't be a hundred percent certain whether she meant existing or additional ones; and Raymond Meadowfoot said he "may have something on" although with his rotund figure and awkward gait he did not, to be fair to him, exactly look the type who would go in for nude modelling.
As a last gambit, I decided to target a sprightly-looking old boy whom I didn't recognise at all. Approaching him, I said "Good morning. Would you like to come and hear our brand new choir on Saturday?" He said nothing but just looked blankly out into space and kept walking. Lucinda Strange, coming up at that moment, said "He'd have difficulty with that, I'm afraid."
Now tiring of feeble pretexts for non-attendance, I gave a mirthless laugh, shook my head and enquired what his excuse was.
"He's going in for an operation on his right ear," said Lucinda.
"And his left?" I asked with a weary sigh.
"He's heard nothing out of that one since 1958," said Lucinda. She patted him indulgently on his shoulder. "Have you, Dad?"

Wednesday 4th June

As if this Saturday's concert wasn't a big enough headache, I was phoned today by Phyllis Aughterlonie to check we were still on for our concert on the 28th June. This one sounded better for my sanity, though: she thankfully is doing the publicity and she says she can guarantee a good audience. She also said that as a choir we could bring up to six guests along and we would all be entitled to join in the buffet. I like that sort of concert.
Had managed to get out of last night's operatic rehearsal on the basis of another commitment, but Mrs Donaldson's dreaded words "See you at ten on Sunday for our all-day workshop" seemed to ring in my ears all day. I'd spent so much time on the phone trying to sell more tickets for Saturday's concert that I'd just had no opportunity to think up a reason

for escaping *The Mikado* that was both watertight and believable. As Katie rightly said, it wouldn't do my credibility or standing in the community much good if I were to advise that I was just leaving on a trek round some of the most dangerous, remote and inhospitable corners of the world, only to be spotted pushing my trolley round Homebase on a Saturday morning.
The fact that according to our ticket sellers we have an audience of just nine for this weekend's concert, which includes Maurice Flitwick's guide dog, didn't affect the standard of singing in tonight's final rehearsal. In fact we were done so early that there was time for us to meet up in the pub where we discussed possible *Mikado* avoidance strategies.
"You could just tell Mrs Donaldson you had a work commitment abroad during show week," said Jack. "I've done that before."
"No good," I said. "Our chief exec's secretary belongs to the group. I hardly have anything to do with her, but I couldn't risk it."
"A pre-booked holiday?" Alison suggested.
"They asked me if I had any leave in September, and I told them I hadn't," I said. "If I tell them I have, they won't believe me."
"I'd just tell them straight you don't want to do it," said Mike. "Just be honest."
"She won't listen," I said. "She never listens."
"Well," said Angus Spadgwick, who had joined us during this conversation,"you could always do what my old friend Colin Appleton did when wanting to get out of a commitment he'd been lumbered with."
The atmosphere became hushed as we grouped round Angus, hoping he might provide the breakthrough I needed so much.
"Well?" I asked.
"It was like this," said Angus. "He really didn't want to do it. Desperate to get shot of it. Just like you, really. But they – the committee, I mean – were determined he was going to go through with it. He asked for a meeting with them and told them he'd just been diagnosed as suffering from an extreme form of vertigo. Obviously he was having them on. But he went to a lot of trouble to make it look genuine. A forged doctor's letter and medical certificate. It was an absolute masterstroke. Checkmate. They released him immediately, saying they completely understood and offering their profoundest sympathy. So if you want my advice, that might be a good tack to follow."
"Vertigo seems an odd reason to pull out of a show," said Mike.
"Oh, it wasn't a show," said Angus. "It was a bungee jump off the roof of the Dellford Job Centre."
"Just go back to counting the bubbles on your Britvic, Angus," said Charlie.

Saturday 7th June

Well, we can't say we didn't try to get an audience of more than sixteen for our first Lambsball Green Singers concert. We'd got a few lines in the *Dellford Chronicle,* avoiding the "Angus' Graveyard column" as Stan put it, and it was purely conjecture that we'd have got more punters in if we'd been described as singers rather than stingers. And following a tentative email to Love It FM we'd got a mention on a show that went out when it was statistically more likely for the majority of the local populace to be awake. It wasn't such a beautiful evening that everyone would have been wanting to lounge in their gardens, nor was it so foul that people felt constrained to remain in their front rooms and subject themselves to two hours of *I'm An Ice Dancer, Get Me Out Of Here.*

Still, at least it meant there was no danger of Elphine, the concert buffet provider, having to rush home to prepare an additional two hundredweight of cheese, bacon and pickle doorstops.

We'd split the programme into two halves with the lighter items in the second. Before we started I was introduced to Sylvia Rhoades-Brown, chair of the local branch of the Samaritans. She asked if we'd like her to say a few words before the refreshment break and I agreed. All I can say is that her dictionary must have had a different definition of "few" from mine and probably most other English speakers. Her initial 5 minutes of thanks to us were certainly very much appreciated. The next ten minutes, devoted to the genesis of the local branch, teetered on the verges of tolerability. But far from satisfied with that, she then felt moved to provide a "case history," as she put it, about "a man we'll call Albert" and his tragic story of drug taking, alcohol abuse, gambling addiction, failed marriage and repossession of Sky digital equipment. A saga which had ended happily as one of her colleagues had persuaded him not to jump from his eighth floor window and convinced him that life in Harold Wilson House, Grimley Road, was worth living after all.

The upshot was that instead of ending part one at 8.20, which my careful planning had concluded we should have done, it was nearly 9 when we adjourned to sample Elphine's buffet. And when the Bishop family, representing a quarter of our audience, said unfortunately they needed to decamp because one of their number was flying out to Mongolia next morning, an emergency rethink of arrangements for the latter part of the evening was required.

"I say we pull the plug on it now," said Charlie, who'd come along to give us some much-needed support. In helping to eat the sandwiches, that is. "Let them make what inroads they can into that mountain of carbohydrate then we can all go to the pub."

"We've still got ten pieces to go," Alison pointed out, "including two of my favourites."

"But you're doing them all again in three weeks anyway," Charlie argued. "For the local winos…..I mean, the homeless people."
"People have paid well to see the whole programme," said Susan. "We're selling them short if we don't finish it. Even if only a few are present."
"Tell you what," said Mark. "I'll go and get the vibes from the punters."
He was gone a couple of minutes, and returned with an ominously long face. "Decision's been made for us," he said. "We need to wind it up now."
"Well, I'm not happy to do that," said Alison. "We've put a lot of work into these pieces and they really are good. Especially that setting of *Country Gardens*."
"True," said Mark. "But what if I told you that Sylvia's thank you speech will be supplemented by the story of how she saved Clementine Bullivant from jumping off Clifton Suspension Bridge after her cat had been run over by a 93 bus."
There was an expectant silence.
"Actually," said Alison at length, "I think Charlie was right. There are only so many doo-be-doos one can take. And there are an awful lot of them in *Country Gardens*."
"And as for selling them short," said Charlie, "they can all take a few sandwiches. Two lorryloads each. If that's not value for their ticket money, I'm the Deputy Chief Town Crier of Nether Wallop."

Sunday 8th June

The first Sunday workshop day for *The Mikado*. And as I write, late this evening, I still have not succeeded in extricating myself. On the contrary, I seem to be in it even deeper than I was this morning, with all the adverse consequences that will inevitably follow for the development of my own singing group.
I duly attended at 10a.m., as instructed, and having started at 10.25 we spent the first hour on ensemble music, including much of my chorus work. Ironically I actually found myself enjoying it, all the more so when Lucy Boustead, certainly the most attractive as well as the most competent singer, took the part of Yum-Yum (my stage partner) in place of the absent Violet Handysides, the old dear who'd not so much been murdering it as toying with it, slowly torturing it and then bludgeoning it to death last week. It got better. After coffee and a very acceptable bacon sandwich, the male chorus was taken aside for yet another look at the moves for the opening chorus, which Madam Jogging Suit – today Madam Oil-Stained T-Shirt Exposing An Excess Of Cleavage And Shapeless Tracksuit Bottoms – had replotted. While they were doing that, I was bidden to sing through all my non-ensemble musical numbers with Lucy and the other soloists, and it was in fact huge fun. For the first time

I actually saw myself doing the part. We were given a decent lunch break, and there was even time for me to pop home and spend some valuable quality time with the Advanced Wordsearch from the Post Roast Workout page of my Sunday paper. I returned to the hall really quite excited about the work that lay ahead that afternoon.
Then, enter Violet Handysides.
The next hour and a quarter can only be described as an hour and a quarter of sheer hell as I was forced to stand immediately next to her during the plotting of some numbers in the middle of Act 1. Her voice was raucous and usually out of tune and her dialogue was stilted and expressionless; even all of that might have been forgivable were it not for her insistence, during sections of dialogue involving the two of us, on draping her arm round me and on one occasion digging into my right hip with her surprisingly sharp fingernails. After receiving one particularly powerful jab I turned to Lucy, who happened to be standing nearby, and said with some feeling "I've just about had enough of this. Goodness only knows what idiot gave her that part. She's a complete liability." Lucy shrugged and said nothing.
As for Violet's dancing, it was even worse than mine, and our movement, when movement was called for, resembled not so much two sprightly young Japanese lovers as two Rymans League footballers chasing a careless back pass. And on 73 minutes, as the ref was about to blow up for half time, some clumsy footwork on my part together with her lack of finesse off the ball, saw my right boot make contact with her left ankle. With a most un-Yum-Yum like squeal, she crashed to the floor – there was certainly no suggestion that she was just diving to get an undeserved penalty kick – and lay there writhing in a helpless heap while the other players called urgently for trainer and stretcher. The match was abandoned and the protagonists were instructed to vacate the field of play, with a rematch scheduled at 7.45pm on Tuesday. To include substantial added stoppage time.

Tuesday 10th June
I am no longer in *The Mikado*.
As I wasn't needed for tonight's operatic rehearsal till nine, I decided to go along to a meeting of the Dellford Happy Harmonists. I soon discovered that a major problem for the group was its name. Although nominally situated in Dellford, it was actually situated in a community hall in the district of North Farrantside on the far side of the town. Far from being happy, all the arriving singers seemed to wear lugubrious careworn expressions as though the thought of spending the next 2 hours in each others' company ranked as an even less enticing prospect than that of an all-expenses-paid 30-year holiday overlooking Guantanamo

Bay. And I can only assume that an emergency Act of Parliament had suddenly redefined "harmonists" as "all singing exactly the same tune below the note and behind the beat." At least I was not requested to join them but sat at the back, prevented from leaving only by my respect for their pleasant welcome and their polite and solicitous concern for a newcomer. Well, that and the promise of filter coffee and home-made cookies in the interval.
My patience was, however, rewarded as, during the interval, I obtained a potential new member. Sarah Lambourn was certainly no spring chicken, but I hadn't noticed any of the more painful squawks coming from her direction; on the contrary, I'd noticed some quite pleasing sounds issuing from her first alto line. She told me she'd lived in Lambsball Green for years, and she said that although she was away from tonight until the 27th she'd love to join our group. Unfortunately the interval was just ending as these welcome words were rolling off her tongue, and as I was anxious to get off to my other rehearsal before being subjected to further feeble attempts at happy harmonisation, I only just had time to invite her, plus her next-door neighbour who she thought might be interested in joining us too, to come to our concert on 28th June as our choir guests.
It was with a light heart that I made my way on to the operatic rehearsal, only to be met at the door by Mrs Donaldson who ushered me into a side room, invited me to sit down, and withdrew from her WH Smith carrier bag a sheaf of dog-eared papers held together by a treasury tag. On the top sheet was the single word RULES handwritten in severe red ink.
"This is a sad day," she said.
I wasn't sure what she meant. There were certainly plenty of developments that day which would distress many. I was aware the latest peace talks in the Middle East had broken down. I'd heard on the radio of a damaging tidal wave in the Gambia. The Bank of England had put up its interest rates and borrowers were certain to be hit hard. And Waitrose in Dellford had run out of Camembert cheese. I awaited further elaboration.
"I'm afraid we're going to have to let you go," she continued. "Your outburst to my daughter during Sunday's rehearsal about the decision to give Violet Handysides the part of Yum-Yum was reported back to me."
"Your daughter?" I said. "The only person I spoke to about that was Lucy Boustead."
"That's right," said Mrs Donaldson briskly. "Boustead's her married name. She's my eldest daughter and assistant secretary of the operatic society. The Committee felt bound to apply rule 28.2 which states that anyone guilty of conduct unbecoming the society, including inter alia quoting from rule 28.2.6b insubordinate or insulting comments directed at or towards or intended for office holders of the society may be dismissed

from the society without notice. I have the Rules here if you wish to peruse them."
Notwithstanding my feeling that the principles of natural justice entitled me to reasonable notice of a hearing and the opportunity to make representations in my defence, I certainly wasn't planning to challenge the decision. I merely wished them luck in finding a replacement singer.
"Oh, we've got one already," she said airily. "Mike Fuggins. I thought he was in Australia but his contract was terminated early. The show must go on!"
With massive relief I drove home and rang Stan to advise him of the outcome, at the same time telling him that I didn't think my comments had been that offensive. and that they'd taken a bit of a risk. "I mean, if this Mike Fuggins hadn't come forward I don't know what would have happened," I said.
"You'd still have the part," said Stan. "He rang Madge Donaldson last night. You don't suppose they'd have booted you out otherwise, do you!" He chuckled at my naivete. "What did you say to upset them, anyway?"
"I just said I didn't know what idiot had given Violet Handysides the part of Yum-Yum," I said. "I don't see why Mrs Donaldson should take such exception to that."
"You would," said Stan, "if you knew who'd made up the audition committee."
"Who?" I enquired.
"Violet Handysides and Mrs Donaldson," he replied.

Wednesday 11th June

Woke up this morning feeling as though a heavy weight had been lifted from my shoulders, and certainly in a better frame of mind to start preparing for the talent contest which I want to take place before the summer holidays. That way at least I can tell what forces I'll have for the autumn and will be able to plan accordingly.
Having spoken to Stan and Charlie, I've gone for the 12th July – one advantage about a village where nothing happens is that there's never a serious danger of clashing with anything – and we've agreed a committee meeting next Tuesday to go into the finer details.
"I've been thinking about judges," said Charlie. "I think it's best if I don't. I really don't want to upset Florence."
I felt like telling him it was a bit late for that now. "Any ideas?" I asked him.
"Quentin Oatway might be the man," he said. "Ex-colleague of mine on the Bench. I'll ask him when I see him at the Silly Old Buffers lunch on Friday."

I thought it might be prudent to seek Stan's opinion. "Well," said Stan, "he'd certainly be an improvement on another Bench colleague, Doreen Phipps, who he suggested might use her Bench experience to judge the last village flower show."
"How do you mean?" I asked.
"Put it this way," said Stan. "If there were 40 different classes to judge in a single afternoon, would you want as your judge someone who allowed her Sunday morning bath water to get cold because she couldn't make up her mind which colour supplement to take into the bathroom with her."

Sunday 15th June
In church this morning I happened to notice that the church magazine had started again. I had a read through – it was all pretty dull stuff, I have to say – and noted that the editor was now one Cecil Small. Afterwards I sought him out and asked if he'd be happy to promote the talent contest through that publication. "Oh, I'm not the editor now," he said. "I was just a temporary stand-in till they found someone who could do it permanently. You need to speak to Aileen Parkins, the new editor."
My heart sank. Aileen Parkins was known as a particular difficult lady, and when I approached her with my piece she favoured both it and me with a stare icier than a National Serviceman's first morning shower. "I should have had this by yesterday," she said. "All copy by the 14th of each month."
I apologised profusely and told her I didn't know who the new editor was.
"Well, you know now," she barked. "I've just taken over from Cecil Small. I thought everybody knew he was no longer doing it."
"Well, I did wonder," I said, thinking that by injecting a touch of humour into the proceedings I might just break through the layer of frost that was caked to her hard, disapproving face. I pointed to page 12 of Cecil's mediocre offering. "I must say I began to doubt his credentials when I read in the last issue that everyone was invited to Juliet Clancy's house for some serious whipping and bondage."
"Whipping and bonding," Aileen Parkins growled. "Juliet Clancy's new cake-making group. And if you must know, I wrote it."
Bang goes that one then.

Tuesday 17th June
To my surprise, Jonathan Perfrement turned up at tonight's committee meeting, and on time too.
"Busy day?" Charlie asked him.
"Not too bad," he replied. "Just cleared 60 emails in the last hour, finished two reports during the morning and the first draft of a

spreadsheet for completion by members of the Operational Targeting Network Group."
"Do you ever take any days' leave?" Angus asked him in wonderment.
"Today *was* a day's leave," said Jonathan Perfrement. "Now, I'm not up to speed with recent committee business, so if I can perhaps have a catch-up. Have we an agenda for tonight?"
"There's no agenda," said Alan. "We're here to plan the talent contest on the 12th July. Loads to do, very little time to do it."
"Perhaps I can help," said Jonathan, removing his laptop, small projector and collapsible screen from his briefcase. "I've just attended a weekend course on proactivity in management. Now I assume you've got your ducks in a row as far as your aims and objectives for the evening is concerned, but I would guesstimate that there's still a number of I's to be dotted and T's crossed and you're all on something of a steep learning curve. Past experience suggests that this isn't rocket science, but that we as stakeholders need to focus, think a bit outside the box and with that in mind I want to run a few ideas past you, utilising a presentation given to us on that course and which incidentally I intend to cascade to middle managers in the coming weeks, and with the benefit of this quality face time, we can then begin the creative process with a thought shower."
"Can you repeat that?" Charlie asked. "In English?"
Within three minutes the hi-tech presentation had begun and from the mundane world of Lambsball Green on a murky early summer evening I found myself transported into the world of Management, where words which had previously presented themselves to me as mundane and matter of fact seemed to take on strange and wonderful new meanings. I'd always believed goals to be things that were scored in football matches, performance to be something that went on in the Royal Albert Hall, customers to be people found queuing in Sainsbury's on a Friday night, mission statements to be the sole preserve of evangelical Christians, and road maps to be documents confined to the glove compartment of the car. And after thirty minutes of existence in this strange parallel universe, I don't think I was the only one to marvel at the possibility, at any one time, of being able to be heads-up, on message, singing from the same song sheet, thinking the unthinkable, ticking the right boxes and keeping my eye on the ball while all the time keeping a watchful eye out for the elephant in the room.
"Now," said Jonathan, "I'm going to ask you to split into syndicate groups and for the next twenty minutes brainstorm amongst yourselves what concerns and issues you are facing in achieving the goals desired for this project. Then we'll feedback in plenary."
"In where?" queried Charlie.
"Plenary," Jonathan repeated.

"Right, thanks," said Charlie. "Is it walkable from here or do I need to bring the car round?"
I nominated Angus and Alan to work with and we duly brainstormed and fed back as instructed – not that it was hugely difficult for me, as I'd already gone through the outstanding issues in my head a dozen times.
"Now then," said Jonathan. "I want us all to decide on ways in which we can overcome these concerns, and in order to gain closure on this part of the process, draw up an action plan setting out objectives that meet the SMART criteria. Can anyone just remind me what SMART stands for?"
"Stupid Managers Ask Ridiculous Things," Charlie retorted.
To his credit, Jonathan didn't flinch an inch but gave us a further fifteen minutes in our groups and, using the flipchart he had presciently kept stored in the back of his car, wrote up the results of our discussions.
"So let's go through these," he said. "By Friday, to ask Elphine to do the catering. By next Wednesday, to have three judges, to ask a well-known media face to attend to open the contest, and to approach the local news media for publicity. By next Friday, to have agreed entry fees, with entrance money going on prizes, appearance money for the personality, and the rest divided between the singing group funds and charity. Well done. An excellent evening's work."
"Yes," said Charlie. "All of which we could have achieved just by a round the table discussion in less than 15 minutes. Instead of which we've been at this nearly an hour and a half."
"Would anyone else like to comment on that?" Jonathan asked which even I, with no training in management or communication skills, realised meant "I'm stuffed."
There was no response to his invitation. "In which case," said Charlie, rising to his feet, "I'd like to utilise a managed approach to run past you a proactive and front-loaded action plan for the facilitation of my expeditious egress from my present workplace environment and effect a step change in my strategy for the medium short term future."
"I beg your pardon?" said Jonathan.
"It means I'm off home to watch the cricket," said Charlie.

Thursday 19th June

Angus Spadgwick rang just as we were beginning our dinner to ask us if we'd like a piece about the talent contest included in his column. I reckoned that if any single factor was going to bring our attendance down to less than a figure of zero, mention in his column was what was likely to do the trick, but with my mind more firmly set on Katie's delicious meat crumble swimming in thick gravy, I told him nothing would please me more and prepared to ring off. But Angus had other ideas.

"I've got one entry for the contest already," he said. "I mentioned it to my friend Bill in Carlyon Street and he said he's got a particularly good talent."
"Oh, yes," I said. "What's that?"
"Give him any year before 1970," he said. "Sorry, I tell a lie – 1969 – and he can say who was number one in the hit parade on Christmas Day of that year."
"Yes, okay," I said, "I can't quite see how that's going to be of massive entertainment value to the punters on the night, but still. Has he been tested before?"
"He went on local radio last year with it," said Angus. "He got a few of them wrong, I will admit, but then got a great deal better. Mind you, the interviewer did make it easier for him."
"How?" I asked, open-minded optimism giving way to fatalistic resignation.
"By switching on the monitor in front of him and bringing up the webpage with all the information on it," said Angus. "He was fine after that."
Made a mental note to write Angus a glowing reference. For when he decides to apply for a job as telesales operative for Overpriced And Totally Energy Inefficient Conservatories Inc. And waste other people's valuable leisure time for a living.

Sunday 22nd June
Phyllis Aughterlonie was in church this morning and after the service I ran through the arrangements for next Saturday's soiree in her garden. She assured me again there'll be a good audience.
"There's just one thing," she said. "I'm no longer working for the homeless project. It turned out that donations to it were being spent by the staff to buy drugs for the people staying there. I'm now supporting another charity that's very close to my heart in view of what happened to my younger sister. I do hope you don't mind."
It made no difference to me. "Not at all," I said.
"I knew you'd understand," she said. "Can I ask how long your programme is?"
"It's about sixty minutes," I said. "Sound about right?"
"We could do with a little more perhaps," said Phyllis, "but perhaps it's best to err on the side of caution. We don't want to bore them, especially when we're relying on their generosity for the retiring collection."
"Absolutely," I said. "Always leave them hungry, eh!" I handed my empty coffee cup back. "By the way," I said, "What is the charity?"
"The St James Foundation," said Phyllis Aughterlonie, "for chronic anorexics."

Tuesday 24th June

Still no nearer finding a celebrity to appear at the talent contest. Time is short as we want to get it on the publicity material and that can't wait much longer. I'd hoped that Charlie, with his many contacts among the great and the good, could help, but he was only able to come up with Clarence Conway, the High Sheriff, and Oswald Bastable, the Lord Lieutenant. And however many lines they may have in *Who's Who, Debrett's*, or the brand new district council publication, *People of Dellford*, available from all good bookshops, council offices during standard opening hours and via the council's website, 20 per cent discount if purchased on line by the 31st July, all major credit and debit cards accepted, I can't see the punters queuing down the street to show off to them their ability to play *Onward Christian Soldiers* with an HB pencil on a line of gin bottles.

It was Alison, one of the singers, who rang me at work today with the best lead so far. "My best friend knows Tina Heath really well," she said. "She starred in *Lizzie Dripping* and used to present *Blue Peter,* do you remember?"

Brought up in the good old days of Valerie Singleton, John Noakes, Getdown Shep *et al*, I had to admit that while the name Tina Heath rang a bell, I wouldn't have immediately made a connection between her and the programme. I decided the best thing was to take a straw poll of our respective offices to see how many people knew of her claim to fame.

And I soon discovered that I was far from alone in my ignorance. Of the 12 colleagues I spoke to, just two correctly recalled her as a former member of the *Blue Peter* team, three reckoned she was a presenter on *Songs Of Praise*, three thought she'd fronted *Swap Shop* with Keith Chegwin, one thought she was married to Keith Chegwin, one thought she was the daughter of Keith Chegwin, one thought she actually *was* Keith Chegwin, and one had her down as the manageress of the Cat And Fiddle in Halliburton Crescent.

Which just left Judy Clatford, our rather overweight human resources assistant. "Do you know of Tina Heath?" I asked her.

"Tina Heath?" she echoed, reaching down to remove a blob of chewing gum from the sole of her left flip-flop. "I think Dan and I might have walked the dog over it the other weekend."

I suppose I've nothing to lose by googling Peter Purves.

Thursday 26th June

Alan and I spoke at lunchtime and agreed that finding a celebrity may be a lot harder than we first supposed. As he says, it's very short notice, we can't honestly say the money from the show is going to charity, and the

fees many celebs will charge might leave us seriously out of pocket. He added "You want to avoid complete nonentities who maybe have had a few minutes of fame and are clearly motivated by the desire to promote themselves rather than anyone or anything else. You can spot them a mile off." I told him I'd bear it in mind.
Tonight, following an afternoon of spectacular nil success in getting hold of Mr Purves or any other former *Blue Peter* presenter, I got a call from a lady who introduced herself as Patricia Jameson. "I gather from a friend of a friend that you're seeking a well-known face to open your talent show," she said. "I wonder if I might be able to help."
I was rather lost for words. "So who are you?" I asked.
"I'm an author," she said. "Romantic fiction. I've had twenty books published, and they've all done very well. I moved to Dellford a few years ago. I write under the name Pat Wentmore."
Not being the greatest fan of this particular literary genre, I confessed that I'd never actually heard of her.
"I think you'll find that a lot of people will have done," she said. "as long as I'm billed on your publicity material as Pat Wentmore, the acclaimed romantic novelist. Don't get me wrong. I'm not just some complete nonentity who's had a few minutes of fame and is just motivated by the desire to promote myself rather than anyone or anything else."
I rather got the feeling I'd heard that before somewhere. But the signs were promising and I was beginning to think we might do a lot worse.
"There is the question of the fee, of course," she went on.
I wondered if this might raise its head. "Absolutely," I said. "I do accept it isn't a charity evening, but I don't think that having regard to the numbers attending we can be looking at anything too extravagant. Perhaps – I don't know how you feel – £25?"
"That sounds fine," she said. "Shall I make the cheque out to you personally?"

Saturday 28th June/Sunday 29th June
Phyllis Aughterlonie's house certainly was delightful. She introduced me to her pride and joy – her pedigree King Charles spaniel Alfred – and asked us to be particularly careful not to leave footmarks on the new rug she'd just brought back from Tibet. The décor was faultless, from the carefully chosen antique furniture to the elegant white screwtop jugs containing iced water, the perfect tonic for dry-throated singers on a balmy evening.
The whole event had been organised with military precision: drinks and canapés, half an hour's singing, a hot buffet(goulash or curry), a further half hour's singing, then cakes, puddings and coffee, and a prompt finish

in time for Wimbledon highlights and Michael Parkinson's latest farewell chat show.

We sailed through the first section of items by eight, and Phyllis announced that we'd be back on again at nine, and no later. "If you're not there, you'll miss it," she said. Definitely my kind of girl. Or would have been, were she 30 years younger. It was almost too perfect: a beautiful sunny evening, a superbly kept garden rendered lush and colourful by the recent rains, and a large and appreciative audience – with the better and more popular half of the programme before us. And already noises were being made about our getting invited back again next year, and the year after that.

As my requested portion of goulash – I'm not a great curry lover – was being served to me, I felt a tap on my shoulder. I turned round to find myself face to face with a woman who did look familiar but whose name, and the context in which we'd met previously, escaped me completely.

"I'm Sarah Lambourn," she said. "You told me I could come tonight as a choir guest with my neighbour Maria. Remember? Dellford Happy Harmonists?"

It all suddenly came flooding back. I placed my plate down and shook hands with them both, then after some very pleasant conversation we fixed up for the two of them to come along for voice tests next Wednesday.

Unfortunately the clock was ticking away, and I still hadn't eaten a thing. Phyllis heaped on the pressure by reminding me there were just thirteen and a half minutes to go before we were back on. Reflecting that Virgin Trains could use someone like her, I told her not to worry, grabbed the plate of food from where I'd left it, found a comfortable seat and took a large mouthful......of what was not goulash at all but the strongest hottest curry that had ever passed my lips.

Noticing a white screwtop jug on a table a few yards away, I instinctively rushed to fill a glass with iced water in order to extinguish the fire that was now raging in my mouth. Having failed initially to coax any liquid from it, I frantically began to turn the screw. Rather too frantically, as it happened, for at that moment, under the pressure of my heavy grip, the whole top detached itself from the rest of the jug, depositing fluid not only from the spout but what seemed like every other orifice in its structure. Not water, but boiling hot coffee which gushed out in liberal streams and splashed down onto Phyllis Aughterlonie's pedigree King Charles spaniel Alfred, who until then had been reclining luxuriously on the new Tibetan rug. The startled animal emitted an agonised yelp, leapt from the now coffee-stained rug and scurried out of the room, directly into the path of Phyllis Aughterlonie, whose fifteen plus stone shot temporarily skywards then crunched down onto the hard stone floor of her entrance hall, a sickening crack coming from the direction of her left ankle, and her head making a forced landing in the middle of a lemon meringue pie.

I stood there, gazing at the scene of total devastation, hardly knowing which disaster area to turn to first. The need for emergency veterinary treatment for Alfred. The need for emergency medical treatment for Phyllis. The need for emergency shampoo treatment for the new Tibetan rug. And the need to break the news to Alison that *Country Gardens* was out again.

It was well past midnight by the time Phyllis was seen in A & E at Dellford General, and nearly one o'clock by the time we got to the emergency vet to enquire as to Alfred's welfare.

"Well," the vet replied, "I suspect he may have to be pulled out of Crufts next year. You can't really enter a dog into Best of Breed with scalding scars all the way down its back. Still," he went on hastily, "It's not all bad news."

I told him I was glad to hear it.

"Yes," he said, "they think the way he sprinted across the room after having the hot coffee poured over him makes him a dead cert for the 100 metres in next month's Dellford Petolympics."

JULY

Wednesday 2nd July

Alan and I called together the committee and all the singers for a meeting tonight, which began with voice tests for Sarah Lambourn and Maria Roberts, both of whom passed with consummate ease. The early abandonment of last Saturday's concert thankfully hadn't stopped us receiving a generous donation to our funds and it was very gracious of Phyllis not only to provide that but to tell us we weren't to worry about the excess on the insurance for the costs of the emergency veterinary treatment. However, one thing we'd originally hoped would come out of the evening was the invitation to do more events – there had, after all, been plenty of influential people there – and of course this had been rather overtaken by the call for paramedics, first aid boxes and quick action stain removers. Anyway, we reckoned the best thing to do was put Saturday's disappointment behind us, and with that in mind we confirmed our concert at the Dolls House Exhibition in September for its patrons and their families, with a donation that'll be divided between the local hospice and our funds. No speeches, no canines, no dodgy coffee jugs – just an evening of music and readings with fruit juice and small nibbles in the interval.

Then we moved on to consideration of the talent show. We've decided against trying to get a celebrity to open the contest on the grounds of economy, and against another leaflet drop on the grounds of preservation of shoe leather, going instead for a generous display of posters around the village which thanks to Mike's graphic design skills will be very easy and inexpensive to produce. The *Dellford Chronicle*, mindful perhaps of the success of the *Britain's Got Talent* TV show, has taken an interest, and I'm seeing one of their reporters on Friday with a view hopefully to a good spread in next week's paper. And better still, I have a daytime slot on BBC local radio next Tuesday on the mid-morning show with Jonathan "Jonty" Halestrap, the self-styled Housewives Favourite, at the BBC studios in Greatmere. We've sorted out arrangements for prizes – vouchers will be purchased from the entrance money and forwarded to the winners after the contest – and I've asked all the members to try and obtain us some good raffle prizes. And Elphine is already on 4am reveille for home-made biscuit preparation. The first four tons are due to be delivered this weekend.

Lastly we went on to consider the choice of judges. Quentin Oatway had told Charlie he'd be delighted to do it; in addition Charlie, notwithstanding Flora's accusations of blatant and offensive stereotyping. has persuaded two other members of the bench to act as judge, one, he pointed out, being "Mr Nice" and the other "Mrs Nasty." Having been given their phone numbers, I rang them later to tell them more about the evening and how we hoped they might contribute. Quentin Oatway certainly seemed an excellent choice of chairman, and having talked to him at some length, I was sure he'd bring just the right mix of dignity and good humour to the evening. Mr Nice certainly lived up to expectations: Peter Westlake was a charming old gent who didn't sound as if he was capable of saying anything disagreeable about anyone. And although Mrs Nasty, Judith Bartley, was perfectly pleasant to me, it rapidly became clear that politically she was well to the right of Genghis Khan and an advocate, in respect of someone unwise enough to be convicted of an offence before her, of a few hours in the town pillory. And that was just for riding a moped without a crash helmet.

Sunday 6th July

Because one of the sidesmen was unwell, I agreed to assist in giving out hymn books this morning. Shortly before the service started Phyllis Aughterlonie hobbled in, and I made a point of going up to her, shaking her hand and saying "You've been very much in my thoughts and prayers this week."

She gave me a smile that radiated kindness and forgiveness. "That's very sweet of you," she said. "I've seen the poster for your talent show. Such a lovely idea and I'd be so happy to try and help promote it for you."

At once I felt a sense not only of real optimism for Saturday but of release from my guilt of the events of eight days ago.... a sense of release which lasted until eight and a half seconds later, when the single hand that was left supporting a pile of twelve hymn books slipped, bringing all of them down onto Phyllis' foot.

It was just a pity it couldn't have been the foot that was already encased in three layers of plaster.

A surprisingly busy and productive evening. Having been interviewed for the *Dellford Chronicle* on Friday, I received by email the draft article, which reads extremely well and should encourage plenty of competitors on Saturday. I also got phone calls offering two or three raffle prizes, including Susan's friend's offer of the use of her holiday cottage in the Malvern Hills for a week, and, from our new recruit Sarah Lambourn, the promise of a home-made iced rich fruit cake. But I have to say I would be surprised if anyone who was undecided as to whether to give up their valuable time to attend on Saturday would be persuaded to do so on the strength of Jonathan Perfrement's pledge to supply the raffle with a copy of his management skills book *Who Killed My Chocolate Biscuit.*

Tuesday 8th July
Arrived in Greatmere in excellent time for the radio interview. I'd never listened to Jonty, as everybody seemed to call him, but first impressions of the set-up generally were very favourable. The producer got my name slightly wrong, although I have answered to David Blakeway – and worse – before, and I had no complaints about the leather armchairs, pint-size mug of latte, apricot-filled Danish and complimentary newspaper. All that was missing was my personal grooming specialist and executive life coach. Three others, two smartly dressed women and a casually attired man, all middle-aged, were sitting with me, each supping their own caffeine-and-calorie-rich beverage, and keeping themselves very much to themselves.
In due course Samantha, the charming production assistant, summoned me into the studio. To my surprise, having entered and shaken hands with the great Jonty himself, I found that the three others in the waiting area with me had all followed me in too. Further handshaking was however forestalled when Jonty said into his microphone "And now the vexed question of the Greatmere Superloo. I have with me here three people who've been campaigning ardently for this facility, the suggestion of which has sparked considerable controversy." Assuming that my interview was to follow on directly after this, I sat and listened while the three guests spoke forcefully about the environmental benefits to be gained by knocking down the existing public toilets in the town, all of which were regularly vandalised, and replacing them with a central, vandalproof suite of toilets, on the site of an empty shop premises. It seemed that the council were opposed to the idea, on the grounds of expense and concern about the blendability of the new loos with the neighbouring buildings. Having heard from the campaigners, Jonty turned to me and said "David Blakeway, if I can then bring you in to react to what you've just heard."
I'd not been listening too avidly, and certainly was unwilling to voice any authoritative opinions, but I obviously had to say something. "Well," I said, "I'm in total sympathy with all three and I have no difficulty at all with what they're asking for."
There were beaming smiles from the other guests.
"Can we quote you on that, Mr Blakeway?" Jonty asked.
"If you like," I said.
"And you'd be content for work to start as soon as possible?"
"I don't see why not," I said.
"I'm sure the campaigners among the listeners will be delighted to hear you say that," said Jonty. "Thank you all very much indeed." He removed his headphones, turned to us and said "Super, thanks guys. Sam will see you out."

And to my surprise, we all suddenly found ourselves being bundled out of the studio and onto the street via a side entrance.
Not familiar with the immediate surroundings, I lost my bearings completely and it was another ten minutes or so before I fought my way back round to the front desk and requested readmission to the inner sanctum of the Housewives' Favourite so that I could actually do what it was I'd come to do.
"I'm afraid whoever you are, you're too late," said the well-endowed young receptionist, whose skimpy vest top left little to the imagination. "Mr Halestrap's got his next guest with him now. They're devoting the rest of the morning to discussion of environmental issues."
"You don't understand," I said. "I've come to talk about the Lambsball Green talent contest. I wasn't here about the Superloo thing."
The woman professed not to know what I was talking about so I explained the situation in greater detail. With a sigh she hauled her somewhat overweight frame off her chair, and landing unsteadily on the soles of her amply heeled sandals, taxi-ed into position and manoeuvred herself off out of sight. A good twenty minutes passed with no sign of her, and with work appointments later that morning that I couldn't put off, I had no alternative but to call it a day and leave.
Idly, I switched my car radio on as I queued to exit from the multi-storey.
"And the top story this hour from our Greatmere studios," said the announcer, "is the district council's dramatic U-turn over the proposed Superloo for Greatmere. David Blakeway, the council member responsible for the environment, has in the past hour on this radio station given his unequivocal backing to this highly politically sensitive scheme, bowing to pressure from local campaigners. His decision is set to cause a huge storm, with reverberations that may be felt in town halls the length and breadth of Great Britain."
On return to my office, I found there was a message on my answering machine from Jonty Halestrap's producer saying she was sorry I'd not been able to make it this morning. "I hope it won't affect support for your talent show," she said.
Just as I hope that the busty receptionist wasn't hijacked and hauled in front of the nearest microphone having been mistaken for Dean of the Faculty of Climate Studies and Biofuel Economics at the Massachusetts Institute of Science and Technology.

Saturday 12th July
Well, we'd certainly been working hard today to prepare for tonight's talent contest, and things were looking good as we opened the doors to punters at six thirty. As we really had no idea how many competitors there would be, we'd planned that we would register the entrants and the

type of their act, and then formulate a running order based on that. As Charlie had impressed upon me the need to "keep the judges sweet, especially Mrs Nasty," registration had to be delegated to Angus in order that I could devote myself full-time to their care. Meanwhile, Elphine busied herself laying out tupperware boxes full of delicious-looking cakes and biscuits in the kitchen, keeping back a special boxful in the committee room for consumption by the judges, while Alan and Debbie set up the electronic keyboard.

Thankfully, the judges all arrived in good time for me to show them in, seat them and offer them a welcoming tipple. As I pulled the chairs for the judges into place, I heard some quite stunning music from the kitchen area. "Who's that?" I asked Angus who happened to come in at that moment.

"That's the Three Fivers," he said. "Three teenage girl singers. Just warming up."

I was elated. "And how many other acts?" I asked.

"Nearly twenty," said Angus.

By the time we got going, there were no less than twenty-four acts and fifty in the audience, consisting not only of those waiting to go on, but well-wishers and family members too. Unfortunately, however, the quantity was not matched by the quality. Whether it was the absence of a celebrity opener that discouraged others from competing, I don't know, but I strongly suspect that the presence of Tina Heath, Keith Chegwin or even both would have raised both numbers and standards. I'd deliberately left what I reckoned would be the higher quality items to near the end, hoping to avoid a sense of anticlimax and loss of interest as the evening wore on, but this meant that during the first half we found ourselves wandering through a desert of dross. Young Alfie Sullivan's attempt at the first page of the first movement of Mozart's *Clarinet Concerto* sounded woefully under-rehearsed, while the scratching noises generated by Leoni Abraham's violin provided a stark foretaste of the horrors to come amidst the hellfires of the next world and thereby a warning to us all to repent of our sins without further delay. Mavis Perrett's dog Puddles, when asked to jump nimbly over sixteen piled-up volumes of the *Encylopaedia Britannica*, gave what in fact was a perfect impersonation of the statue of Greyfriars Bobby. Josephine Looseley, Marjorie Bentham, her brother Rupert, and Victor Cartledge produced a spoken *Geographical Fugue* which went off course somewhere near Budapest and was last seen preparing for an emergency landing in the southern reaches of the Kalahari. The Great Magnifico, alias Percy French, proved popular enough as an incompetent magician, but the poor chap in the audience who donated a £50 note which disappeared might at least have expected it to turn up at some time before the end of the act. And as for

Arthur Elderton's Wheeltappers-and-Shunters-Social-Clubesque anecdote, delivered in cod Yorkshire accent, I'd felt a closer affinity for the sights, sounds and smells of the Doncaster back street working men's club during my college work experience placement at Marks & Spencer in Tunbridge Wells.

Throughout it all, the judges were remarkably tolerant and diplomatic, especially Judith Bartley who had ample opportunity to live up to her "Nero The Second" billing that Charlie had accorded her. Still, at least the wholly unriveting nature of the entertainment allowed me to think ahead with a relatively uncluttered mind to the interval and the sufficiency of the fare provided. There were more people present than I'd expected, so, having ascertained that all three judges had eaten before they'd come out, I took the decision to add the judges' box of goodies to the competitors' buffet. I noticed Alfie and his Year 8 classmate Leoni looking rather bored, so asked them to nip to the committee room, collect the box and pass it to the kitchen helpers.

As Charles Pratt finished his supposedly "wickedly funny" political dialogue with his glove puppet Tootles, which actually raised as many laughs as an EU debate on minimum packaging requirements for the export of butternut squashes, I announced the end of the first half and advised that refreshments were available in the kitchen. As the punters wandered off in that direction, a tall ruddy-cheeked man in his thirties came bounding up to me.

"Where the hell's my box?" he screamed.

"Box?" I echoed.

"Yes!" he shrilled. "I left it in the committee room when I went to the gents. I came out and it was gone. Where the hell is it?"

"Just a minute, just a minute," Quentin Oatway interrupted. "What's so important about this box?"

"It's not the box itself," said the new arrival. "It's what's in it. A twelve-foot long boa constrictor, that's what's in it."

"What are you doing with twelve-foot long boa constrictors in this building, you prize idiot!" screeched Judith Bartley, showing her true magisterial teeth for the first time that evening.

"Snake charming," was the reply. "I told your dopey bloke at the front desk when I came in. I think he thought I was going to sing something. Now, for the last time, where have you put the damned thing!"

"Well, the only thing that's been moved out of the comm....oh my goodness!" Suddenly the same ghastly reality seemed to strike all four of us. Together with the snake-charmer we all dashed for the kitchen – Peter Westlake showing more energy and animation than at any time since we'd started – in order to attempt to remove this potentially lethal addition to the interval buffet table. But it was too late; from within the

kitchen area I heard a barrage of truly blood-curdling screams and the next moment there was a panic-stricken rush of bodies in all directions. Worse, in the general melee the snake owner found himself unable to get into the kitchen, which gave the wretched reptile, presumably itself startled by the hysterical reaction to its presence, time to slither out of its box and temporarily out of sight. Impulsively we yelled at everyone to clear the building. Game over.
Fortunately once calm was restored, the reason for the evacuation was found reasonably quickly and placed back in captivity. Leaving just myself, Angus, Alan, Debbie and Quentin Oatway. Peter Westlake had presumably gone home for a gin and tonic, and Judith Bartley was no doubt assembling an emergency court sitting and convening an off-the-peg firing squad in anticipation of my conviction for aiding and abetting the escape of dangerous animals from lawful custody.
"Well, then," I said. "Who do we award the prize to?"
We considered. There hadn't been a single entry in the first half of the programme that merited any sort of favourable recognition. The best sounds I had heard all evening had been from the Three Fivers, whose contact details Angus had mercifully retained. We thought it over, and decided there could be only one outcome.
"So that's it," I said, a few minutes later. "The Three Fivers win the talent competition. Without actually having taken part."

Sunday 13th July

To my annoyance I found that in the confusion of last night I'd allowed Angus to go off with the list of contact details of the singers who were due to perform in the second half of the talent contest. I'd not intended to go to church this morning but having rung Angus six times between nine and nine fifty and got the engaged signal each time, I decided it would be quicker just to go along to church, where I was sure I'd find him, and ask him in person.
Fortunately Angus was not only in church but had the list with him. "You've even got one in church this morning," he said. "Look, the last one on the list." He pointed to the entry he'd written, FRANK GROTTY – 'GRANDMA'S FLANALET(sic) NIGHTSHIRT,' and indicated a T-shirted beer-bellied man near the back, whom I did vaguely recognise from last night as one of the more enthusiastic audience members.
After the service I approached him. "Hi," I said. "Mr Grotty, I believe."
"Give it a rest, will you," he said with a grimace, and a moment later he was gone.
I looked helplessly at the woman who'd been sitting next to him. "Was it something I said?" I asked her.
"Yes," she said. "His name. It's Crotty, not Grotty."

I knew I should have delegated a different albeit equally responsible talent contest task to Angus last night. Staying as far away from it as possible.

Monday 14th July

Well, to my delight, the talent contest has indeed done exactly what I hoped it would do, namely generate new members from among those who previously wouldn't have been the least bit interested.

Thankfully I did manage to get through to Frank Crotty on the phone at work today. He was very forgiving and told me he shouldn't be so sensitive, having had to put up with this unwelcome variation on his name for most of his fifty-two years. He told me he's lived in the village all his life and worked in it virtually all his adult life too; he restores old wooden furniture, and has just finished a major facelift on a memorial bench to the late Cuthbert Longstock in the main street. Apparently Mr Longstock was a resident of the village who made an outstanding contribution to community life during the middle of the last century. Having dutifully sat through the history lesson I invited Frank to come to our next meeting for a voice test. I also spoke to Kirsty Lovegrove of the Three Fivers, congratulated her and her colleagues on winning the talent contest, and asked if they'd like to come to the next meeting to be tested as well. She replied that she, Becky and Jasmine would love to get involved, subject to their other musical and study commitments. And providing there are no pythons or black mambas in town at the time.

Which just left Percy French, a name that was strangely familiar. I then realised that he was the Great Magnifico, the worst magician and Tommy Cooper impersonator in the world. He obviously fancied himself as a singer as well, as he, like Frank and the girls, had expressed a wish to give us the benefit of his vocal range in the second half of the programme. I finally got through to him this evening, and having told him through gritted teeth what a great act he'd put on for us on Saturday and what a shame we'd never got to hear him sing in the second half, I asked him if he'd recovered that £50 note.

"Oh, my goodness," he blurted out. "I completely forgot about that."

Having spoken to Stan I ascertained that the owner of the note was one Simon Greybridge, and I wasted no time in ringing him to ask if he'd got back the note he'd donated to the Great Magnifico. "No, I haven't," he said.

Three hours, at least another dozen calls and a frantic search round the Assembly Room including an unexpected and unwelcome diatribe from Edna Mudge about snake droppings in sugar bowls later, I was forced to ring Simon Greybridge and tell him we'd been unsuccessful in recovering his money. "But it's okay," I said. "We'll see you get your money back."

"I wouldn't worry," he said. "I gave him £50 in Monopoly money. I wouldn't trust that joker Percy French with a Computers For Schools voucher, let alone fifty quid."
Reflected, as I trudged upstairs to bed, that there was very little I would not do in order to avoid putting myself through another evening like this one again. And there would certainly never have been a better time for me to have been approached to head up a team of volunteers tasked with watching the creosote dry on Cuthbert Longstock's seat.

Thursday 17th July
Certainly very satisfying now to have a singing group of seventeen, if you include the new recruits and those like the vicar and Duncan Adams who can't promise to be there all the time. It's still not quite as many as I'd like, but I've a nice balance of singers: Alison, Karen, Susan, and obviously the Three Fivers Kirsty, Becky and Jasmine on soprano, Gail, Sarah and Maria on alto, Duncan, Frank, Mark and myself on tenor, and Mike, Jack, Alan and the vicar on bass. But I'm still looking for more, and this isn't the best time of year to be doing so.
Was pondering how I could boost our ranks over the summer when Geraint, the vicar, rang up sounding very excited.
"You'll never guess what's just happened," he said. "A quite astonishing revelation." I assumed he was referring to a deep spiritual experience or mystic vision of divine power, but perhaps I should have known better. "I've discovered that next month it'll be the 80th anniversary of the first timetabled bus service through Lambsball Green. I've spoken to George Ridler and he's agreed to let us have Parker's Field for a bus festival next month. The 16th, to be exact."
"Bus festival?" I echoed.
"Yes," Geraint went on. He sounded like a child who'd just discovered his presents under the tree on Christmas morning. "I've been on the Internet and the phone all day, and I've arranged for a number of vintage buses to be on show, all of which we'll use for bus memorabilia. We'll have refreshments, cream teas, a band....and I'd like to bring in the singers. Doing some entertainment suitable for the occasion."
I have to say I couldn't immediately think of a great many songs on a bus theme. There's Flanders & Swann's *Transport Of Delight*, one of the funniest songs ever written about bus travel, but that was written for two voices, not seventeen. And there's the children's song *The Wheels On The Bus,* but I fancied that Duncan Adams wouldn't be too chuffed about taking precious time out from his high-powered business commitments to stand in a field proclaiming that The Horn On The Bus Goes Beep Beep Beep All Day Long. However, it seems that although Geraint would like there to be a few ditties linked with wheels of some description, he is

happy for us to do a selection from our existing repertoire – we may even get to do *Country Gardens* – and we can perhaps use it as a recruitment opportunity.
"I'm sure there'll be a good take-up," he said.
It's nice that he's so optimistic. But from my own experience of bus travel and bus enthusiasts, I suspect that take-up is as likely to be about as high as on an offer of a One Out Of Three Go Free deal for ballooning holidays over Baghdad.

Sunday 20th July
The smallest attendance I'd ever witnessed for a Sunday morning service at St Augustine's, with a lot of regulars away on holiday. Apparently it's not likely to pick up till September. Geraint announced that he himself will be away next Sunday on what he calls a "refreshment and renewal weekend" – subtle code, apparently, for a miniature bus exhibition in Droitwich – but gave a lengthy plug for his own local bus event next month, promising it will be "one of the most exciting things to hit Lambsball Green in years." But to judge by the expressions on the faces of the 30 or so of those present, he might as well have been advertising the imminent state visit of a Slovakian tax inspector with hepatitis C.
I was asked if I could help with coffees afterwards, as two of the regular helpers were amongst those who were away. Although I wasn't exactly thrilled at the prospect, as Katie and I were going out later, I reflected it might be a good way of getting to know people better, feel more accepted in the church and thereby build up contacts which might in turn yield more singers. But my prospects of becoming an established member of the post-worship beverage provision team suffered something of a setback when, as I was washing the cups and mugs afterwards, admittedly with rather more vigour than was perhaps advisable, the handle of one hideous yellow mug with some Oriental writing came clean off in the washing-up water. However I suspected it wouldn't cost much to pop to Tesco and replace it.
Better news, however, was being told by my co-helper Rosemary that she was the member of a society I had no idea existed – Dellford Amateur Dramatic Society, or Daddies for short. They disbanded two years ago but have recently re-formed and there are one or two Lambsball Green residents amongst them. They've broken for the summer but will be meeting up again on 2nd September. I told her I'd put it in my diary at once.
As we were finishing, Alice Embleton came into the kitchen. "Just coming in to collect my mug," she said. "The bright yellow one."
"The yellow one," I echoed. "I hope it wasn't too precious."

"It's my most treasured souvenir of my visit to Japan," she said. "It's quite irreplaceable."
I somehow think that's me off the coffee rota. For about the next three centuries.

Wednesday 23rd July
Committee tonight, preceded by the voice tests for our new recruits which thankfully were formalities. A welcome to Duncan, who's agreed to join us as singers' representative. And apologies from Angus Splodgewick, engaged on last-minute tinkering to his latest Column That Nobody Reads And Even Fewer People Talk About, and Jonathan Perfrement, detained at the last minute by a meeting of the Lots Of Caffeine Fuelled Chit Chat But Achieve Absolutely Nothing Steering Sub Committee.
After a rather gloomy post-mortem on the talent show, I broke the news about the vicar's bus event.
"Well, I have no issues around it," said Flora. "I support anything that brings the village together and promotes a wider understanding of our respective roles as community stakeholders."
"It'll bring the village together all right, Fenella," snorted Charlie, "saying that it's time the vicar was back in the funny farm where he belongs." He turned to Elphine. "I dare say he'll ask you to cook up some traditional bus station fare," he sneered. "Onion butties, soggy chips and tea at 85p per slice."
There was a long silence. Although Charlie has a thoroughly unpleasant way of putting things, I couldn't help feeling he was right about this one. It had the makings of a disaster. The silence was only broken by the explosive sound of Edna Mudge blasting her way into the room armed with mop, bucket and scrubbing brush which she slammed down onto the floor with such force that the whole room seemed to shake on its foundations.
"Don't mind us," said Charlie affably, as the needle on the Assembly Room seismograph jerked back to somewhere nearer the bottom of the scale.
"It's not my fault," Edna snapped. "That Mr Fothergill of the council. Insisted on a meeting here this afternoon at barely two days' notice. It's put me right out and I won't have it." Her last words were accompanied by the banging of the head of her mop on the bucket, setting off a further disconcerting series of tremors which once more startled the pigeons from their nests on the roof and had our coffees dancing miniature hornpipes in their mugs.
Notwithstanding this unwelcome disturbance to the peace, Alan gamely began to articulate his thoughts on the vicar's proposal, but gradually he became drowned out by Edna's vigorous mopping interposed with her

TEA
AGENDA

increasingly frequent gasps and grunts the like of which I'd not heard since I'd inadvertently gone into studio 1 rather than studio 3 of the Odeon and found myself watching the climax of *Emmanuelle 2*. Finally, Alan gave up the struggle. "Could you please just bear with us one second, Edna," he said.
With bad grace, she threw her mop across the room. "Well," she said furiously, "all I can say is, if you're that keen to attract some attention, why don't you all just dress up as bus conductors and clippies and turn it from a real farce into a total shambles."
"That's it!" Charlie exclaimed, springing to his feet. "That might just work! We make the whole thing a period piece. Say the forties or fifties. Gents as drivers, girls as clippies. Punters would love it. Edna, my dear, I could kiss you."
Not that that latter course of action was really to be recommended. Unless Charlie actually fancied ending his days being ground to powder and sprinkled over Edna's Staffordshire bull terrier's nightly three tinfuls of Lassie Meaty Chunks.

Thursday 24th July
Was on the phone to the vicar today asking if, with his bus contacts, he could assist with the provision of a set of period uniforms. He asked me to leave it with him and rang back with a number of possible leads, most of which he'd got off the Internet. Unfortunately the majority of them proved useless, the only one able to promise me anything being a costume agency in Penrith, over three hundred and fifty miles away.
Still, it was good to have all our singers save Mark and Susan – away on holiday – there tonight, and even better that they are now so supportive of the bus event, attracted rather than put off by the prospect of singing in uniform. And everyone is really keen to do at least two or three concerts in the autumn.
When I got home Katie told me that one of the vicar's suggested contacts, Barry Huskisson of Greatmere, whom I'd had to leave a message with earlier, had rung back. I returned his call immediately.
"I understand you may be able to help me with bus conductors' gear," I said.
"Well, we're able to help with all sorts of things, dearie," he replied in a voice that made Larry Grayson sound like Russell Crowe. "I have a *very* nice clippie's uniform. Peak cap, white shirt, optional brassiere, jacket with shiny buttons, clip-on tie, navy blue knee-length skirt, dark stockings….oh, and of *course*, the sensible brogues."
"Just the one?" I enquired.
"Yes, just the one, luvvy," said Barry. "Now, would you like it or would you not? We can hire it by the week or by the month. Refundable deposit,

payable before delivery, refund conditional *on* safe return of aforesaid item."

I hesitated. It still left us with at least a dozen to find, but then again, I supposed that one was better than nothing.

"Okay," I said. "Would you be able to deliver it?"

"I can do, darling," he said, "but I thought you might want to come over in person. So you can try it *all* on first."

Actually, I quite fancy a trip to Penrith.

Sunday 27th July

During a violent thunderstorm on Friday night, rainwater had leaked in through the roof of St Augustine's, so this morning's service was relocated to the village school. The fold-up chairs with shiny metal bases were certainly a lot more comfortable but the congregation was, if anything, even more feeble than last Sunday's. However, one very welcome bonus was the fact that Jane Stranks, the head teacher at the school, was present to supervise proceedings. She isn't a regular at St Augustine's – well, let's face it, not many people in Lambsball Green are – but this seemed a golden opportunity to establish a more solid contact between our singing group and the school, following the virtually non-existent response to my overtures in February. We agreed before the service that we'd have a chat afterwards over coffee.

It was another lack-lustre service, the promise of coffee just about the only thing which made it worth my while staying, but in due course the act of worship drifted to its close, coffee was served, and I sat down in my comfortable chair next to Jane Stranks.

"So, tell me about your group," she said with an encouraging smile.

"Well," I said, but got no further than that. Aware that I was slouching down in my seat a little, and not wanting to appear disrespectful, I pulled my posterior more towards the back of my chair, taking the rest of my body with me. What I hadn't bargained for was the back of my heels catching the metal base of the chair in front, which jerked backwards across the slippery-smooth school hall carpet. The result was that the lady who expected at that moment to place her own backside on the chair in question found it making contact with fresh air instead, and a split second later it hit the floor with a sickening thump. Fortunately Jane Stranks, used to dealing with the unexpected during the course of her school day, was able to administer the necessary first aid, and no long-term harm was done. But it certainly did not enhance either the process of bridge-building between singing group and school, or my already fragile relations with Alice Embleton, whose rump it was, especially as yet another of her coffee mugs was consigned to an early grave.

Still, I was fairly sure that there would not be quite the same antique or sentimental value in this week's vessel. Commemorating the 1989 promotion of Dellford Warriors C Team to Division Three(North) of the South Western Under 55's Dominoes League.

Monday 28th July

Better news about the bus uniforms. Having spent some time on the Internet myself today, I located a company, curiously enough on the outskirts of my old town, which specialises in the provision of costumes to amateur operatic and dramatic societies. Having secured their assurance that they can kit us all out, I rang Geraint later and he confirmed I can claim back all the costs of the hire from the day's takings. All we need to do now is to go over *en masse* for the fitting.

Pleased to have achieved this breakthrough, I duly put together a draft programme and rehearsal schedule for our two "slots" which will be at 2.15pm and then again at 4.15pm, comprising in each case really nice arrangements from the lighter side of our repertoire. Where I've struggled is in locating some transport-related pieces. I've found, again using the Internet, an *a cappella* version of Flanders & Swann's *Transport Of Delight*, but I couldn't come up with anything else and the emailed suggestions I'd requested from group members have borne singularly little fruit. I don't recall *Hope & Keen's Crazy Bus,* apparently a children's sitcom from the 1970's, let alone the signature tune to it; I do remember watching *Here Come The Double Deckers*, but again, apart from the "See you next weeeeek" bit at the end, how its signature tune went completely escapes me, and I doubt it's available anyway; and I've no desire to trawl through every Nancy Sinatra CD collection to try and locate and set for unaccompanied voices her 1971 Top Ten song *Did You Ever* notwithstanding the inclusion of the line "Hey I know just the thing for us; no, not now, I'll miss my bus."

Tonight I got a phone call from a man by the name of Kelvin Robards. He told me he'd got my number from Flora Sandstrom.

"Basically," he said, "I've written what I describe as a secreligious piece."

"Don't you mean sacrilegious?" I queried.

"No," he said. "I mean, basically, it's like a sacred oratorio, with solos, recitatives and choruses, but is entirely secular and humanistic in nature. It's called *To The Glory Of Glory.*"

"So where do I come in?" I asked.

"Basically," he said, "I'm looking for a choir that can perform this work and give it the impetus it needs to become established as a major choral piece. And as one of our Humanist Society members, Flora, is giving so

much to your organisation, it seems only fair that you could give this to us in return."
I told him I'd have to see it first and asked if we could meet up to discuss it face to face next Tuesday when he'd have the music with him.
"That's okay," he said. "Perhaps if I just basically gave you an idea of the piece now it'll inform our discussion next week." Without waiting for me to comment, he ploughed on. "It starts as a hymn of praise to the wonders of the natural world and to the mysterious forces that have shaped our universe from beyond infinity. It then explores and deplores the way man has ravaged and abused the human and natural resources that surround him and failed to learn lessons from the past to inform decisions about the future. It damns the hypocrisy and divisiveness of religion and its power to damage the human soul and corrupt people's hearts and minds by proclaiming absolute dogmatic values in the face of diversification of philosophical thought. And finally it offers a new hope for the peaceful advent of human reason and rationality, transcending racial and cultural barriers, breaking free of the languid trammels of bigotry and idolatry and providing for a new and dynamic framework for humankind's relationship with the natural order."
"Er....yes," I said diffidently. "There wouldn't be any mention of buses, would there?"

Thursday 31st July
The month has finished on a remarkably positive note. After further extensive enquiries on the Internet – taking up time I'd like to have devoted to some pre-summer holiday recruitment – I've found a Japanese-made mug which is pretty well identical to the one belonging to Alice Embleton, and I should have it within the week. It's certainly pricey but I was pleased to have made the effort for a fellow church member. Despite the enforced curtailment of our chat on Sunday, Jane Stranks has used her influence to obtain for us a new singer, an alto, from the newly-constituted Parent Teacher Association, and although she can't do the bus bonanza she'll be with us from September. Alan's fixed up a concert at the Dolls House Exhibition for the end of that month, so there's something to look forward to following the break I've suggested we take for the second half of August.
And tonight we had a good rehearsal of some of the music for the 16th. The vicar, bless him, spent almost every spare moment filling us in on further details of the event, from the exact age and make of each bus on show to the precise tonnage of the day's supply of scotch eggs, cold sausages and treacle flapjacks, the preparation of which is already prompting Elphine to set her alarm for three forty-five in the morning.

“If you want my opinion, the man’s definitely got a screw loose,” Mark muttered as we prepared to leave at the end of the evening.
I have to say I like Geraint and felt almost duty bound to defend him.
“I think you misjudge him,” I said. “He’s just very enthusiastic about his subject, that’s all, and is anxious to transmit this enthusiasm to others and by so doing foster a real sense of community spirit which can only be good for the village as a whole.”
The vicar called me over to him a second later and asked me what I thought of his draft poster for the bus event. I glanced at it and noticed the starting time was stated to be 10.53am. I asked him what was wrong with 11am when I thought we were kicking off. “Oh,” he said, “it’s to coincide with the exact time of the very first bus from the corner of Philpott Road.”
Mark was right. Totally barking.
“And what about the finish?” I asked.
“That’ll be at 5.20pm,” he replied. “The time of the last bus to leave the village on the same day. No twenty-four hour clocks in those days, eh!”
I suppose we should be grateful for small mercies. That the instigators of the inaugural bus service hadn’t laid on a Theatregoers’ Late Night Special.

AUGUST

Sunday 3rd August

Yet again we were at the school for our worship this morning. To my surprise, Flora was there together with her grandmother. The service, with a congregation of just twenty-eight, was marginally better than last week's, although the fact that the vicar's announcement of the finer details of the bus event was longer than the sermon perhaps gave an idea of his spiritual priorities.

Over coffee afterwards I told Flora I'd been contacted by Kelvin Robards, and she seemed genuinely pleased when I said I was meeting him this week. "He's a really good bloke, David," she said. "I think if you can use his piece you'll get a good audience for it – among a lot of my humanist friends for a start – and that'll be great news for the future of the group."

We chatted quite animatedly for a while and I found myself actually warming to her for probably the first time and reflecting that maybe there were ways in which we could work together in the future for mutual benefit. Relaxed and confident in her company – that being a first as well – I looked across the hall and asked "Didn't you say you went to this school, Flora?"

"That's right," she said with a smile.

"You must have been to a few assemblies here in this very hall," I said.

In a split second, her own pleasant disposition was replaced by what was, in my eyes at any rate, her more familiar "I have issues with you" countenance. "I'm sorry?" she said, blinking at me.

"I just said, you must have been to a few assemblies here," I said.

She looked at me as though I was a five-headed six-eyed monster from the planet Zog who'd stepped out of his space capsule and requested a guided tour of the town's council tax recovery office. "I never attended assemblies," she said. "My parents withdrew me from them on humanistic grounds. They were unhappy about my being forced to pay lip service to the values and tenets of a belief system they had chosen to reject and about which I was too young to make my own decision."

I stammered an apology and thankfully found a distraction in the form of a request by Angus for some help conveying a stack of chairs into the cupboard adjoining the hall using a two-wheeled transporter. I placed the flat metalled base of the transporter under the chairs and tugged at the handles in order to tip the chairs towards me, ready to wheel them to the cupboard – only for the entire pile of chairs to tip outwards, away from me, in all directions, the top one knocking a coffee cup clean out of Alice Embleton's hands. A plain cup this time, so it was impossible to tell from a cursory glance at the tiny brown-stained fragments whether I'd just been responsible for the untimely demise of a piece of exquisite 17th

century hand-crafted genius fresh from a guest appearance on *The Antiques Roadshow* and now boasting an insurance value of £5,000, or a chipped reject from the Army & Navy Stores warehouse boasting an insurance value of ten pence.
But whatever its value the expression on Alice Embleton's face suggested if she had her way she'd follow Flora's parents' example. And withdraw me from any event with any religious content whatsoever.

Tuesday 5th August
Tonight I went round to Kelvin Robards' house, a small detached bungalow at the end of Franklin Road. Kelvin welcomed me, introduced me to his partner Martin, and ushered me into his sitting room at the back of the house. I was invited to sit by the window, within easy reach of a shelf crammed with books on environmental issues, and within easy smelling distance of the rotting fruit and vegetable matter that was piled into a huge compost bag situated in the garden beyond.
"Here it is, basically," said Kelvin, producing and opening a box file labelled TO THE GLORY OF GLORY on the outside and containing a frightening amount of paper inside. He removed about half a dozen pages and invited me to take a look at what he described as the "really powerful" opening chorus.
Although I'm not necessarily the most discerning judge of what makes good music and what doesn't, three things struck me immediately. The first was the legibility, or rather the lack of it. It really did look as though a couple of spiders had staggered away from a pot of particularly intoxicating ink and decided to see how much of the page they could crawl around before they finally keeled over. The second was the prodigious number of key and time changes in just the first two pages, and what at first sight looked quite complex harmonies that I feared might be a little beyond the ability of most of our singers. And thirdly was the number of repeated sections, it being by no means clear where one actually had to repeat from, the general confusion not alleviated in the slightest by little scribbles here and there instructing singers to "go to bar 23, third time," "sopranos hum in verse 4" and "omit bars 1 to 5 and bars 6 to 8 for first repeat." I couldn't resist making the point that it wasn't easy for potential singers to find their way properly round it and suggested that it might have been easier to have written the whole thing out in longhand.
"Perhaps," he said, "but paper is a very valuable commodity and the more we use, the more lives we're putting at risk by the destruction of the rainforests. Basically, I couldn't reconcile a work bemoaning man's damage to the natural order with practices that are blatantly environmentally unfriendly."

That may be so. But I think in some ways I'd rather be prepared to give up an extra thousandth of an acre of South American woodland and be lambasted by ecological pressure groups worldwide as Public Enemy Number 1 than present to the group a piece of music for which we'd have to provide an accompanying satellite navigation system. Or a sackful of working crystal balls.

Thursday 7th August

We all went over to my old town to try on our bus conductors' and clippies' outfits. I have to say that although we felt a bit self-conscious to begin with, and were wondering what on earth possessed us to give up a lovely summer's evening to make ourselves look like "complete berks," as Jack pithily described us, it certainly reinforced our sense of team spirit and it has redoubled our anticipation of what should be a real fun day next Saturday.

Afterwards we all decided to go for a pub meal, and headed for one of my favourite country pubs a few miles away. It was perfect: beautiful summer sunshine, a superb hillside setting, an extensive menu and range of beers, and really good company.

I was just on the point of putting in my order for the lasagne, seasonal salad and French fries, happily looking forward to the oaty summer fruit crumble and creamy custard as my afters, when my mobile phone rang. It was Kelvin.

"Just basically wanting to know if you can give me a definite answer on whether your group is prepared to do my piece," he said.

"It's a bit tricky, Kelvin," I said. "I'm out tonight and I was hoping to look at it over the weekend."

There was a long silence. Eventually Kelvin, in an obviously very disappointed tone of voice, said "You did tell me you'd have decided by tonight and I really need an answer so I can get it in the Southern Humanist newsletter. Basically, the editor's waiting on an answer tonight and won't hang on any longer. If we don't get it in the newsletter we might as well forget it."

I didn't want to commit myself without another look at it. With a heavy heart I cancelled my food order, apologised to the singers, drove home, withdrew from my bookshelf the box file containing Kelvin's *sine qua non* and lifted all the pages out of the box. Unfortunately the volume of paper was far greater than I expected, and moments later they were slithering out of my hands and forming a carpet of white all over my study floor. In the absence of page numbers I could only guess at the right order. It was not for another hour and a half that I had them in what appeared to be a logical sequence, completely overwhelmed by the sheer volume of music but also intensely puzzled by the fact that so many sections seemed so similar and, at times, so repetitive. By now it was ten o'clock and there was just no time to make a proper assessment of the quality of the work. But at least I had a perfectly good pretext for deciding not to do it, namely the fact that it was just far, far too long, and anxious not to keep Kelvin hanging on any longer I rang him up with the bad news.

"It's certainly a very exciting and challenging piece," I said, taking care not to make any reference to its merit. "And I'd like to think we'd be up to it musically. But I'm afraid the problem is the length. I sang a few bits and based on how long it would take to get through the average page, I calculated it runs to about seven hours."

"Seven hours?" Kelvin echoed. "It's fifty-eight minutes, and that's basically only if you do all the repeats."

"But we'd never get through all the pages in that box file in that time," I pointed out. "It must run to about three hundred and fifty pages in all."

"No," said Kelvin. "It's fifty pages. Written out seven times."

I was momentarily lost for words. And not just because he'd delivered an utterance without mentioning the word "basically." When the power of speech returned, I endeavoured to assert myself as best I could. "The problem is, Kelvin," I said, "that I didn't know that, and I can't just say yes to a piece I've not had a chance to look at properly tonight. And you want an answer now, don't you?"

"Well, actually, I've just spoken to the editor," said Kelvin. "He says basically there's a delay with some of the other material. It can wait till next week now."

Which of course made me feel much better about the sacrifice of my lasagne, seasonal salad, French fries, oaty summer fruit crumble and creamy custard in the company of good friends in an idyllic country pub garden in favour of a hastily defrosted submarine roll topped with Stork margarine and the last three slices of ham from a month-old Tesco's budget pack. In front of parts three and four of a repeat of a five-year-old edition of *Wife Swap Australia Revisited.*

Sunday 10th August

Alice's mug had arrived in the post yesterday and I really would defy anybody to tell the difference from the one I'd broken. The cost – in excess of £60 to include postage from Japan – was greater than I'd expected, but I decided it would be worth every penny not only to see the look of delight on Alice's face but to hear her begging me to join the ranks of the coffee-makers and stay there until carried away from the kitchen in a wooden box.

We were back in church this morning and so I took the mug along with me. I couldn't see Alice at first so plonked myself beside a pleasant very

well-spoken woman who told me she was holidaying in the area for a couple of weeks. I saw her titter slightly when Geraint made what was his final Sunday's plug for next Saturday's event, indicating that he was expecting a fair number of groups of enthusiasts from West Yorkshire.
Accordingly I leaned across to her and said "Imagine that. Our village being overrun by cloth caps and whippets for the day."
Instead of smilingly expressing her agreement, she regarded me coldly and said "As it happens, I was brought up in a mining village just outside Rotherham. We don't take kindly to being stereotyped in that way so kindly keep your Southern witticisms to yourself."
I think we can safely rule her out of the queue for Elphine's freshly-made lard and mushy pea doorsteps.
After the service, I located Alice and went up to her.
"I've got a little surprise for you," I said. "Take a look inside this box."
She withdrew the mug. "That's nice, dear," she said. "You've got one just like mine."
"No, no," I said. "This is for you. To replace the one I broke."
"Oh, you didn't need to do that, dear," she replied. "I bought an identical one last week on EBay. Four pounds ninety-five."

Tuesday 12th August
I was able to get away from work reasonably early tonight, so spent some time looking at Kelvin's piece, and playing bits of it on my miniature keyboard. Although my little instrument is hardly the best guide to what in terms of musical quality separates Mozart's 40th Symphony from *Variations On The Theme To Postman Pat*, I could quickly tell that his piece was as discordant and tuneless as it was difficult to read and follow.
I rang Kelvin and having got his answering machine – somewhat to my relief, I have to say – I left a message telling him that for various reasons I didn't feel able to agree to perform his work.
Half an hour later the phone rang. It was Flora. "I've just heard," she said. "I'm devastated."
"It wasn't an easy decision, Flora," I said.
"Did you run it by the committee? By the singers?"
"To be honest, I didn't feel the need," I replied. "It's my group and I have to make a decision in the group's interests."
"I'm sorry," said Flora, "but I have huge issues with that. Your whole attitude is just completely dictatorial, dogmatic, bigoted and frankly offensive. The least Kelvin can expect is for the whole group to look at it and decide.You may be in charge of the members but I for one am deeply pained with the idea of your riding roughshod over their sensibilities."
I imagined the members would find that fairly painful as well.

"I mean, of course, I can share it with the group if you like," I said. "We're meeting on Thursday."
"Well, just remember two things," said Flora. "One, all the work I've put into your committee thus far, and will continue to do. And two, your standing and reputation as a group. Do you want to expand your profile and versatility and almost certainly your membership too, or do you want to stick rigidly in your comfort zone, afraid of a challenge, afraid of ideas that don't sit easily with your own belief systems?"
I caved in and told her we'd all discuss it in two days' time. In principle, of course, her arguments are perfectly valid. But, as I told Katie over dinner later, I still think we'd stand a better chance of expanding our profile and versatility, and being of better overall value to the wider community, by a rendition of the procedures for applying for corporation tax rebates in Uzbekistan.

Thursday 14th August
Although we were only supposed to be holding a singing rehearsal for Saturday tonight, I thought it prudent to ask the full committee along as well so we could demonstrate to Flora just how fair and open we were being in considering Kelvin's piece. Jonathan Perfrement couldn't make it, and indicated that it'd be unlikely that he'd be able to make many more meetings in the near future, having been co-opted onto the REIMATAG – the Regional Executive Infrastructural Management Task Group – or, as Katie put it, the NEFPOJATTE – the Newest Excuse For Pointless Jollies At The Taxpayers' Expense. But Flora was there, and not entirely to my surprise, so was Kelvin.
I was determined to get the singing done first, in anticipation of lengthy discussion on the merits of Kelvin's piece. It was an excellent sing which boded really well for Saturday, and it made me feel incredibly optimistic about the future of the group and quite sorry to be leaving it all behind for a fortnight; Katie and I go off on holiday on Sunday and won't be home till the last day of the month. We're meeting again on the 10th September and will be meeting every Wednesday during the autumn.
After we'd finished work on the Saturday pieces, we turned our attention to Kelvin's composition. He had brought extra copies, meaning only a few of us had to share, and Alan's wife Debbie kindly provided the necessary keyboard accompaniment. I suggested we looked, initially at least, at the grand finale where there was at any rate one reasonably clear melody poking through the otherwise discordant morass. Fortunately there were enough sight-readers amongst us to have a reasonable stab at it, but the sound generated was still somewhat less pleasing than I'd expect if I ever chanced to drop my laptop into the washing machine in midspin.

When we finally got to the end of it, there was a chilly hush, and with Kelvin present, nobody seemed quite sure what to say.
"It's certainly different," said Susan.
"It's a very adventurous and ambitious piece," added Mark.
"Really most imaginative and groundbreaking," Jack chipped in.
"So heartfelt and candid......worthy, really worthy," Sarah observed.
"Bold and sincere," Mike decided.
"Utter crap," said Charlie Tompkins.
"I'm sorry?" Flora said dangerously.
"Well, what's the point of pussyfooting around it, Flavia," said Charlie. "If we don't say it our audience will. All minus five of them. I propose we don't take this apology for a piece any further, but we give a percentage of the proceeds of the next concert to your outfit. Everyone's a winner."
"I'm sorry," said Flora again, "but I just find that monstrously offensive. The whole point of the piece is to promote a positive and relevant message attuned to the needs of the community and encourage a holistic approach to the issues facing wider society."
"And that ends the latest lecture from Freda Sandcastle of the South East Essex Polytechnic School Of Sociotwaddle," sneered Charlie.
"Well, thank you very much," Flora snapped back. "I think this is it, don't you? I've had enough of the lot of you. I'm resigning as of now. Come on, Kelv." With that, she rose to her feet and swept from the room, Kelvin following somewhat self-consciously in her wake looking suddenly less like an ecowarrior than an obedient puppy.
I wasn't too happy about the way Charlie had spoken to them but I couldn't deny that their departure lifted the atmosphere quite significantly. We agreed that now Flora had left us and Jonathan couldn't be relied upon, there was little point in having separate committee meetings, but the remaining non-singing committee members, Charlie, Angus and Elphine, will join our Wednesday rehearsals as and when needed to assist with the planning of future events and discussion and resolution of other issues, including financial matters. We also decided that we shall continue, for want of a more imaginative name, to call ourselves the Lambsball Green Singers and market ourselves as such. Afterwards in the Welldiggers we drank to the success of our new streamlined administration and resolved to redouble our collective efforts to recruit at least eight more singers during the autumn.
Despite that, my conscience was still nagging me, and although it was twenty to eleven when we emerged from the pub, I felt I really did need to ring Flora to apologise on behalf of the group for the way things had turned out. Accordingly, as soon as I arrived home I got straight on the phone to her. "I just wanted to say how grateful we are for all the help

you've given us over the past few months," I said. "I really didn't want it to end like this and I'm sorry you were spoken to the way you were."
Thankfully she seemed in a forgiving mood. She told me she appreciated my calling and the thought behind it. She added that she liked to think that her association with us had caused us to consider cultivating a more tolerant appreciation of the wide-ranging strands of thought that existed within our locality, and that she looked forward to seeing the group embracing a long-term corporate strategy which embraced and celebrated cultural and ethical diversity.
But it remains to be seen whether when we meet in future she'll have ceased to look at me as though I were a frozen portion of caramelised pilchard fritter.

Saturday 16th August
Although we only had two slots during the bus bonanza, I had agreed with Geraint that I would run a stall for the entire day advertising the Lambsball Green Singers, offering bookings and requesting members, and whilst I didn't expect to recruit many people, I reckoned it would be good PR for us.
Whatever shortcomings Geraint Collymore has as spiritual leader and guide, he certainly could not be faulted for his efforts in getting publicity for the event. We were slightly later arriving than I'd hoped, and when we got there I found the place already full of people who were obviously greatly enjoying themselves in the lovely sunshine. There was something quite fascinating about the array of old vehicles that were on display, complemented by a wide variety of side attractions which gave the whole event the feel of an old-fashioned country fair.
I quickly found Geraint, looking very dapper in his cream jacket, purple waistcoat and spotty bow tie. I'd never seen him look so alert and business-like. "Welcome, welcome," he said effusively, shaking me warmly by the hand and giving Katie a kiss on both cheeks. "Come and be introduced to Gertie."
I didn't know anyone called Gertie, but it soon transpired she wasn't a person but a beautiful old 1950's double-decker Southdown bus, which we would be using as our recruitment stall for the day. Geraint advised me that most of the vehicles had been transported by lorry from museums and exhibitions, there being no possibility of their ever being able to be driven again, but there were some, including "good old Gertie" as he described her, which were still driveable today. Indeed, he said, many of them had been driven from their usual places of residence by those responsible for them. All of the buses, he told me, had either been restored for today to look exactly as they had been in their prime, or

contained exhibitions or attractions of their own such as refreshments, sales of local produce and even sideshows.
"So who's responsible for Gertie?" Katie asked.
"Oh, that's Roddy," said Geraint. "You'll find him in the beer tent."
At that time I didn't really appreciate the significance of that remark. Still, I was honoured when Geraint entrusted us with the keys to the vehicle and told us that we were welcome to keep our recruitment stall open for as long or short a time as we pleased. He said we could also use the bus for rehearsing if we wished, prior to our performances on the main rostrum at the top end of the field.
The next couple of hours were certainly educative, if nothing else. It quickly became apparent that the vast majority of the punters were either locals who were well aware of our activities and had chosen for whatever reason not to get involved with them, or visitors to the village who were passionate about all things to do with buses but who had little interest or knowledge in things musical and for whom Liszt was something you took to the supermarket on a Saturday morning, Chopin was something you did in the supermarket on a Saturday morning, Bach was an animal noise and Brahms was the busty shop assistant in *Are You Being Served.* However a number of people took one of the leaflets Mike had prepared on his PC so I didn't feel we'd wasted our time completely. I was beginning to feel quite an affection for our vehicle – not that I could actually bring myself to call it by its Christian name – and with no sign of Roddy at any stage during the morning, I felt very much responsible for it and was almost sorry to leave it for our first selection of music early in the afternoon. It went exceedingly well, with polished singing, perfect tuning and faultless enunciation. It was just a shame that because our performance coincided with the Punch and Judy show taking place at the other end of the field, we had an audience of less than a dozen. Geraint saw how disconsolate we looked, but assured us that there'd be no such clash for our second slot and he'd personally make sure we were very well supported for it, even if it meant closing down some of the attractions for the purpose. "Keep lots of your leaflets handy," he said.
As I returned to our adoptive home I saw a man being carried away from the beer tent, grunting and muttering incoherently and drooling at the mouth, in what appeared to be a state of terminal inebriation.
"Who on earth's that poor guy?"I enquired.
"That'd be Roddy," said Geraint. "Mind you, it's an improvement."
"How do you mean?"
"Last exhibition, he was unconscious before the beer tent even opened."
Geraint was about to go off again in order, as he put it, to renew his acquaintance with Penelope, a splendid Royal Blue coach from the 1960's, when a large jolly-looking man with a walrus moustache and

smartly attired in a striped suit came striding up to us. "I think I owe you an apology," he said.
"Oh, why's that?" I asked.
"I believe we stole your audience. I'm the Punch and Judy man, you see. Eric Scrimshaw. I got my timings mixed up. Entirely my fault."
"Oh, well, these things happen," I said politely.
"I'll try and time the next showing so it doesn't happen again," he said. "No hard feelings, eh?" And the next thing I knew, he was extending his hand. I felt rather embarrassed.
"Very sensitive fellow, Eric Scrimshaw," said Geraint, as the aforementioned gentleman walked guiltily back towards his booth which in fact was situated opposite our bus just across the field. "Hates to think he's upset anybody. Very lonely man. Always lived alone. That Punch and Judy is his life, you know. You might possibly go across and see the show later. Give him a bit of a boost."
I made a mental note to do so. Indeed, over the next thirty minutes there was the opportunity to make a triplicate note in copperplate handwriting, as the average number of "hits," to coin an expression from computer technology, per ten-minute period plummeted from a barely respectable two point seven eight to an ignominious, albeit at least more mathematically satisfying, zero. However, I was jerked from what I feared might be irretrievable languor by a loud thumping sound on the back of the vehicle. Thinking it was a couple of village louts with nothing better to do, I went round to remonstrate, only to find a burly middle-aged man with a red face and sweaty brow, puffing on a small white cigarette.
"You're on my land," he pointed out, indicating the rear of the bus which was protruding onto the adjacent field by what could not have been more than twelve inches.
"I'm sorry," I said. "Is there a problem?"
"There is, as it happens," he said, dropping the remainder of his cigarette and squashing it inelegantly with his left heel. "I'm harvesting at the moment and a dirty great combine harvester could be coming round here any time. I wouldn't like to have to slice the rear off your old Southdown bus. I don't suppose its owner would be too chuffed either. You've only got to move it a couple of feet or so – I'm sure that's not beyond the bounds of human endeavour."
"I see," I said. "I don't suppose it could wait till the fair's over, could it?"
I might as well have suggested he swam a hundred lengths of the Thames Estuary wearing a leopardskin bikini. "This is my livelihood you're talking about," he said. "I'm warning you – move it now. Before my combine harvester does."

Aware that Roddy would be of little use in shifting the bus, I was about to go and seek Geraint's advice when Stan made his suggestion. "I think you could move it yourself," he said.

I gently reminded him that the bus was parked on a slope and releasing the handbrake would simply take it further down into the belligerent landowner's field.

"I don't mean that," said Stan. "I mean you've got the keys. You could inch it forward. I'd do it myself, but I've had a few drinks and I can't risk it."

It was here that I made what in retrospect might be termed by the military as a tactical blunder. Although I wasn't convinced that moving a vehicle twenty-four inches across a field was likely to test his faculties, or trouble the local constabulary, to any great extent, I decided there was little point in arguing with Stan and accordingly I hauled myself into the driver's seat. I actually felt quite excited and wondered if we'd have got more custom if we'd offered bus rides on this magnificent vehicle to anyone showing even a polite interest in joining our group. The first two of the three keys on the ring didn't fit, but the third slid into the ignition lock with no difficulty. I turned the key and with a roar the Southdown sprang into life. Placing my foot on the clutch pedal, I engaged first gear, brought the pedal up and released the handbrake.

And then it happened. As the handbrake went down, the bus, instead of easing away from its erstwhile resting place, shot forward like a lion being released from its cage after being forced to sit through four consecutive hours of Richard and Judy. I slammed my foot on the brake pedal, but absolutely nothing happened and the bus, now on a downslope, forged ahead, on a collision course for the Punch and Judy booth. Poor Eric Scrimshaw collapsed in horror as the vehicle, now out of control, met the flimsy theatre head on, tossed it onto its side and crushed it nonchalantly into a sorry mangled heap. In desperation I switched off the ignition and applied the handbrake but these manoeuvres availed me little. The bus skidded violently, slid down the bank immediately behind the spot where the Punch and Judy stand had been, smashed through the fence separating the field from a row of allotments and ploughed into a wooden shed immediately beyond the fence, uprooting the shed and sending its walls, roof and flooring flying across the surrounding vegetable patches. Our precious double-decker Southdown bus, now finally forced into a stationary position, was left standing majestically but impotently amongst the rows of carrots and cabbages.

Mercifully the occupier of the allotment, though on the site, had not been in the shed at the time but a good twenty yards or so from the final resting place of the bus and such pieces of his shed as had confined themselves to his own patch. But it was with an expression of understandable shock and

perplexity that he tottered towards Stan and me in the bus, evidently quite unable to take in what had just happened.
Stan poked his head out. “Hallo,” he said. “Lambsball Green Singers. Would you like one of our leaflets?”

SEPTEMBER

Monday 1st September

Things had been so hectic during the evening following the bus bonanza debacle that I hadn't had time to put pen to paper and, once on holiday, I forced myself to place the Lambsball Green Singers to the back of my mind, put my diary to one side, and properly unwind. It's really only now, after two lovely weeks away, that I feel ready to return to my diary and begin to catch up.

The good news was that following its unscheduled encounter with parts of Lambsball Green other buses could not reach, Gertie, though hideously battered and bruised, had been duly extricated. And although Norman Snettisbury, the allotment owner, had decided not to take us up on our offer to him to join the Lambsball Green Singers, he reassured me that he'd been about to pull the shed down and we'd actually saved him a job. But that was about all the good news there was during the latter part of that fateful Saturday.

As soon as I got home, I had to ring all the members of the group to apologise for the unforeseen cancellation of the second section of singing, owing partly to my own absence but rather more potently the fact that the sight of a 1950's double-decker Southdown bus sitting in the middle of a vegetable patch was always going to attract significantly more punters, and naturally more media interest, than our own unique version of *Oh Mr Porter What Shall I Do.*

Next on the agenda was a visit to Dellford General Hospital to meet Eric Scrimshaw, bearing a box of chocolates, a hastily downloaded wholesale price list of Punch and Judy booths, and a heartfelt assurance that revenge for stealing our audience was the last thing on my mind as Gertie had steamrollered his pride and joy into oblivion.

Then was the phone call to a company I learned from some of Roddy's more sober friends to be Gertie's insurers, in the course of which, having spent 45 minutes waiting for the 24 Hour Speedy Express Premium Hotline to answer, I was told that according to their records the most recent policy for the vehicle in question had expired in September 1968.

Lastly was taking a phone call from Roddy himself, telling me that although there had indeed been a number of buses on our display which were roadworthy, Gertie emphatically wasn't one of them, and although her acceleration skills were above reproach, her clutch was fiercer than a jilted rhinoceros and the braking system as efficient as an amnesic Sicilian waiter.

So there it was. One wrecked puppet theatre. One fence section converted to firewood. One allotment shed in pieces. Many pounds worth of vegetables and plants destined for the compost heap or the bonfire. One

Southdown bus reduced from a gleaming and valuable attraction for lovers of our transport heritage to a scratched muddy mess. An embarrassingly large amount of coverage of the whole sorry incident on the late local news, thanks to the press interest in the bus bonanza Geraint had secured prior to the event. And the reputation of the Lambsball Green Singers, mentioned as the hirers of the bus in question, now about as solid as a slab of blackcurrant jelly being gawped at by Godzilla.
But things looked up when, having got back from what had been a wonderfully relaxed holiday, I checked my answering machine messages this afternoon. The first was from Geraint telling me that as a result of an incident at a bus show in 1986 involving a display of priceless china and a rampant red Routemaster, all bus shows were now normally covered by the London & General's Special Heavy Machinery Display Accident Policy and after what he described as a "lively" conversation with the acting assistant deputy claims manager of London & General, they had to concede that none of the damage I'd caused at the Lambsball Green event was uncovered by the policy and they would pay out on everything. Then there was a message from the alto Jane Stranks had mentioned at the end of July, Christine Walshaw, saying she was still very keen to join us, and I rang to offer her a voice test after next Wednesday's meeting. The other five were all from local residents who'd seen our news coverage and were now interested in joining the group: Jim Cranwell, Patience Drummond, Rhiann Hodgson, Betty Crabtree and Marjorie Price. Alan and I agreed that we'd give them all voice tests next Wednesday as well, and having rung them back to confirm, I phoned Stan to see if he recognised any of the names.
"You'll be fine with Rhiann," said Stan. "Lovely girl, and good-looking."
That certainly was an excellent start.
"Next, Jim Cranwell did you say?" Stan went on. "Very enthusiastic."
"I'm glad to hear it," I said. "But I take it that's the polite version."
"Er – yes," said Stan. "He sings everything twice as loud as he needs to."
"What about Patience Drummond?" I asked.
"She's got formidable assertiveness skills," said Stan.
"Meaning?"
"If she gets upset about something, nobody gets a moment's peace. Next?"
I sighed wearily. Already I was beginning to regret getting on that plane yesterday afternoon. "Marjorie Price," I said.
"Ah," said Stan. "Marjorie is.....tremendously powerful."
"Translated?"
"She's 22 stone in weight," said Stan.
"And Betty Crabtree?"

"Ah, yes," said Stan. "Very keen horsewoman. In the days of the Lambsball Green WI she used to ride to all the meetings. She still does a lot of riding round the village."
"And what's her voice like?" I asked.
"You'd be better off with the horse," said Stan.

Tuesday 2nd September
To the Dellford Amateur Dramatic Society tonight. The evening could not have been more tedious: a very lengthy discussion about the choice of plays for the year after next, followed by a blocking rehearsal of the first six pages of their current project, involving just six or seven of the twelve present. It was only at 9.15, with the evening's work declared to be concluded, that coffee appeared and things looked up significantly. Rosemary, having provided me with not only a cup of coffee but a delicious slice of fruit cake, introduced me to Derek Samuelson, who lives in Lambsball Green and apparently is really keen to join the Lambsball Green Singers. Derek, though no spring chicken – I was told he was in his early fifties – had a large friendly face, a slight lisp and a raucous laugh, and gave me a vigorous and hearty handshake. Providing he could get through the voice test, which we agreed would happen on Wednesday along with all the others, there seemed no reason why he wouldn't make a welcome addition to the group.
"Yes, I'm really looking forward to singing with you, if you'll have me," he said. "In fact, I hope we might be able to help each other."
"How's that?" I enquired.
"Well," he said, "I've written a play with a Christmas theme. It's gone down really well with my local Playwrights' Group and I'm told there's a good chance of getting it published by a specialist drama publisher. I'm really anxious to see it performed. It doesn't need a huge cast but there are some sections in it which need a chorus. I was wondering how your group would feel about providing the chorus which naturally I'd be happy to be part of, as a new member of your group."
I said I'd certainly consider it. I didn't want us turning into an operatic society, but if all we had to do was to provide choral backing, that sounded manageable enough.
"That's brilliant," Derek said. "I can't tell you how excited I feel. I was so devastated when the Dellford group rejected it when it was put to the vote last year. I lost out to *Midsummer Night's Dream*."
"Well, that's fairly formidable competition," I said. "But even Shakespeare had to start somewhere. What's your play called?"
"The Strange Case Of The Exploding Christmas Puddings," said Derek.

Sunday 7th September

At church this morning Geraint asked us to do something we'd done a few months back, namely to go and make ourselves known to someone in the congregation we'd never met before. Always looking for potential new members on the right side of retirement age, I "targeted" a pleasant-looking woman two pews back, dressed attractively in a long brown leather coat, and asked her who she was.

"I'm Margaret," she said, "as I told you the last time we did this."

Alan was in church this morning and he, Geraint and I had an informal planning meeting after the service to consider our events this autumn. We've got the Dolls House Exhibition concert for the museum's patrons and their families on the 27th; we've pencilled in, extremely faintly, the self-destructing-Yuletide-fare drama for the end of November; and we'd like to do two carol concerts, one in the church with a sacred feel, and one in the Assembly Room with an emphasis on more secular pieces. We also agreed it would be grand to provide a choir for the midnight service.

"What about carol singing round the village?" I asked.

"We could do," said Alan, "but it's another evening out for everyone. And it's really hard work. Not to mention pretty unpleasant if it's wet."

"Well, I might have a solution," said Geraint. "The High Sheriff. He lives on the edge of the village, as you probably know, and he always has a big Christmas dinner for the local bigwigs in early December. When I met him the other week, he said he'd like a group of singers to serenade the guests with seasonal music as they come in. Call it high-class busking if you like. He'll give us a very generous donation. One venue, no worries about the weather, minimum time commitment."

"Sounds brilliant," I said.

"As long as we get one crucial thing right," said Alan.

"What's that?" I queried. "The length of the programme? The content? The number of singers?"

"No," said Alan. "The door."

"The door?" Geraint and I echoed in unison.

"The door," Alan re-echoed. "A few years back we spent three separate evenings practising songs to welcome guests for Dellford's annual traditional Mayor-Making ceremony. After waiting around for half the morning we finally went in and found we'd been standing outside the wrong entrance."

"And the mayor had already been made?" I asked.

"Yep," said Alan. "Made, left to cool, garnished with paprika and served at room temperature."

Wednesday 10th September

An excellent first meeting back, with some good preparatory work done for our Dolls House Exhibition concert and everyone quite happy with what we'd agreed on Sunday. A busy autumn awaits.

Then it was on to the voice tests. Derek disappointingly was suffering with a bad cold and was unable to make it. Christine Walshaw, the recommendation from Jane Stranks, was very sound. Jim, a tall man in his early forties with rosy cheeks and an even rosier chin – one guessed from slight overenthusiasm with a disposable razor – was indeed far louder than he needed to be, but he was in tune, enunciated well and was obviously extremely keen. A good start. Rhiann came next: a very striking young lady indeed, with an extremely tight orange top, short denim skirt and heavily varnished toes thrust into generously-strapped gladiator type sandals. She rather reminded me of Jane Markwick, on whom I'd had a serious crush before meeting Katie. Like Jane, she had an engaging smile and an excellent voice. Marjorie certainly was every bit as huge as Stan had warned me, but thankfully the carpeted floor of the Assembly Room on this occasion supported her generous weight, added to by the half-packet of chocolate digestives I saw her demolishing as she was waiting. I expected her to be a complete disaster, but her voice was absolutely fine and it only needed a Union Jack patterned dress in size 63 and we could have had our very own Last Night Of The Proms.

Then we heard Patience Drummond, a tall, elegant lady with glasses, wearing an immaculate white blouse and long dark skirt. She was the one who Stan warned us had a somewhat assertive character, but whatever skills she may have boasted in that department, her voice was disappointing to say the least with a particularly suspect upper register. I did think that having failed those WI singers back in April, we'd sent out a clear message to the Queens of Wobble in the village, and neither Alan nor I wanted to be compromised on this. He knew exactly what I was thinking, and as she neared the end of her mediocre interpretation of *Linden Lea* he scribbled on a piece of paper in front of me "Polite or blunt version?"

Anxious to avoid any more fainting fits on the Assembly Room floor – particularly with Marjorie standing in dangerously close range – I ticked the word "polite." Accordingly, barely had she finished her rendition than Alan said "I'm so sorry, you're not quite what we're after. But thanks for coming."

Rather than retire gracefully, she just stood there with a look of incredulity on her face. "That's it, is it?" she said.

"Yes, that's it," said Alan.

"Thank you," she said, before walking smartly from the room.

After everyone else had gone, Stan wandered up, jangling the keys, obviously anxious to lock up. "That was okay wasn't it, Stan?" said Alan. "I felt I handled that all right, didn't I?"
"Yes," said Stan. "You were very brave."
I didn't like the sound of that, but before I could ask what he meant, he'd gone to wheel in Betty Crabtree. Well, not quite literally wheel her, but this diminutive white-haired lady dressed in yellow looked distinctly unsteady on her pins even though supported by a walking stick. She told me she'd had a riding accident a month or so ago. I didn't expect any vocal fireworks, and we could only watch in embarrassment as she stood silently through a keyboard solo intended merely as accompaniment for the only song she claimed to know, *Jingle Bells*. When the song – or what should have been the song – came to an end, there was an awkward silence.
"Er – right," said Alan at length. It was the most complimentary response to such ineptitude that one could possibly have imagined. "Have you just temporarily lost your voice, or have you come here by mistake?"
"Oh, no," she said. "I want to join you but in a non-singing capacity. I thought I could help you with some secretarial duties. Did nobody say?"
Obviously it had been shouted to us from the rooftops and announced on the six o'clock news, and I should consider myself solely responsible for this particular waste of my time. Ranking in terms of pleasurability with queuing all night in the pouring rain to buy tickets on my Barclaycard to see Wolverhampton play Manchester United in the Cup. Only to find they didn't accept Barclaycard.

Friday 12th September

Spent some time on the phone this morning talking to Betty Crabtree. She certainly isn't the brightest lamp in the street but is very keen and could have some useful contacts. Having agreed it with Alan, I offered her the post of Lambsball Green Singers secretary which she gladly accepted.
I got a phone call this afternoon from a client, Barry Frost, who hinted to me that he might have a very exciting opportunity available to our singers, namely the possibility of taking part in an *a cappella* concert in the Albert Hall. Apparently a choir that was going to participate has had to pull out, and they're urgently looking for a replacement choir. He said he'd ring me back with more details when he got home from his long weekend away but would be likely to be needing an answer almost immediately.
Later, I got a call from Derek inviting Katie and me over to his house for a drink with him and his wife Paula this evening, principally to be provided with a copy of his play for me to look at. Not quite such a tempting proposition as Barry Frost's, but we were free this evening so I

was happy to accept his kind invitation. As we drank sherry and nibbled at tuna sandwiches in his spacious drawing room, he went quite extensively into his playwriting career and told me that *The Strange Case Of The Exploding Christmas Puddings* was actually his tenth dramatic work – albeit the first he has felt good enough to offer to an amateur dramatic society.
"Having said that," he added, "if this one goes well, I'm quite interested in blowing the dust off some of the earlier ones and seeing if they're viable too."
He reached up to the middle shelf in his bookcase and brought down a bundle of scripts, the top one bearing the title *On Wood Chris Chan Sold Jars.* I instantly recalled dreaming up this contrived play on the title of S. Baring-Gould's famous hymn during an idle moment at St Basil's four years ago, never imagining it would re-emerge on a book cover. "Do forgive me," I said. "That's a weird title for a play. *On Wood Chris Chan Sold Jars*. What's it about?"
"Ah," said Derek, "that was my first work. I decided it would be fun to write a drama with an eyecatching title involving some punning wordplay, then writing the work round that. It was all about a jam jar salesman called Christopher Chan."
"Where does the wood come into it?" I asked, beginning to wish I'd never started this conversation.
"Well," said Derek, "he.....no, I don't want to spoil it for you. Take them all home with you to look at. It may be a cure for insomnia, if nothing else, ha-ha-ha!" And moments later, a capacious Jiffy bag, containing all his previous plays as well as the one he was seeking to inflict on the Lambsball Green Singers, was thrust into my hands.
When we got home, I took out *The Strange Case Of The Exploding Christmas Puddings* and found I was missing large sections of the work including, tantalisingly, the concluding pages. And from what Derek had deigned to provide me, I was left agonising, as I tried to get myself to sleep, about whether the devilish architect behind the final, fatal piece of plum pud was the vicar, the butler, the dotty colonel or the man who'd come to inspect the drains.
Still, the Jiffy bagful of scripts including the epic adventures of Chris Chan did indeed do the trick and gave me my first decent night's sleep in weeks. Being just the right size to shove under our rattling bedroom door.

Sunday 14th September

Katie and I had been out all yesterday and much of today, and it was only tonight that I got the chance to ring Derek and ask him why I was missing so much of the script of the play. He explained that as he wasn't expecting us as a group to provide any of the speaking parts – he had a

number of fellow thespians both from the village and the drama group itself who would provide those – he'd given me just an edited version of the complete script with the chorus work and preceding dialogue so we could see the context of what we were going to be singing. "I've marked all the chorus material in bright yellow highlighter pen," he explained.
Donning my sunglasses, I looked at the script once more. My second perusal of the material provided me with precious little reassurance that I'd been anything other than extremely rash to express even the most cursory interest in it. The fundamental problem, it seemed to me, was that there appeared to be no reason for the chorus to be there other than to get in everybody else's way; they certainly didn't appear to take the story forward at all and simply prolonged what already seemed to be a lengthy and often rambling piece. And as far as the content was concerned, despite extensive searching through each and every page of the material Derek had supplied to me, I found no clue as to what music was to be sung to the words provided. But I dare say Derek will help us to find the right way to communicate in music his scintillating lyrics, starting on page three with our advice to the audience that 'Oh, someone is coming to blow our Mina up, we know they are, we know they are, to blow, to blow dear Mina up.' Andrew Lloyd Webber and Tim Rice must be quaking in their boots already.

Tuesday 16th September
An extraordinarily frustrating day today. My top priority was contacting Barry Frost, who'd still not got back to me following his call on Friday, but despite numerous efforts to contact him, I could only get his mobile voicemail. All the while my work was piling up so I decided to put Betty Crabtree to work and ask her to agree the finer points of the Dolls House Exhibition concert on the 27th including what time we can get in to rehearse, whether they can help us with stewarding on the night, and whether we need to bring our own tea and coffee. From the way she responded to my requests I wasn't massively optimistic she'd taken it all on board, and it was not surprising, but no less annoying, when she phoned half an hour later to tell me there was a problem.
"It seems they're not expecting us on the 27th," she said. "The lady I spoke to, Mrs Pollington, says they've a Mothers Union autumn fayre on the same afternoon. She thinks it won't be possible to have them both the same day. I've got the number of the fayre organiser if you want to contact them."
Infuriating though it was, especially with so much work to do, I had no choice but to sort the whole thing out myself, and make contact with Sylvia Boothroyd, the organiser of the autumn fayre. After a full 40 minutes' speaking to each other's answering machines, we finally found

ourselves next to our telephones at the same time and agreed a pact which a legal draftsman could not have bettered. It required a good 50 minutes to do it, taking into account rheumatic Avril Tuddenham's need for extra time to dismantle the hook-a-duck stall, Lionel Higgins' predilection for spinning out the raffle draw into the small hours and chief-drier-up Constance McElligot's uncanny ability to let fragile crockery slip daintily through her fingers and end up on the floor in a thousand pieces. But we got there. Not, unfortunately, before Barry Frost rang to say that after three unsuccessful attempts to call me in the previous three quarters of an hour, the Albert Hall deadline – already set back specially for us – had passed and we were now too late. I could have wept.

Still, although it was no consolation whatsoever, at least I could now ring Betty Crabtree to tell her all was well and she could proceed with the rest of the arrangements.

"Yes, I will," she said. "There was just one other thing. Mrs Pollington queried whether Monday was a good night for a concert."

"It's not a Monday," I said. "It's a Saturday."

"You did say the 27th October didn't you?" said Betty Crabtree.

As I feared. Useful as a foot masseuse at a mermaids' health farm.

Wednesday 17th September

Although our rehearsal tonight was necessarily short, as three or four of the group had to get off early, we had a good sing, going through the Dolls House Exhibition programme for the 27th. All the new recruits we'd accepted were there. Derek made it to tonight's rehearsal, so after he'd passed his voice test I asked him to talk us briefly through his play and our role therein. I secretly hoped that he would do such a hopeless selling job that the group would agree not to waste any further time on it. My hope, however, was in vain. Whether or not it was out of politeness, or the fact that he's gone ahead and engaged a cast and a booking for the Assembly Room on the 28th and 29th November, I don't know, but there was a good deal more support for it than I expected. Moreover, Debbie seems quite happy to accompany us on our keyboard which Derek said would be more than adequate. The upshot is that as a group we've agreed to go ahead with it. Thankfully, we will only need to attend rehearsals in the final week, so it's not a massive time commitment. But with so much preparation needed for the seasonal events in December, we couldn't have offered any more.

I took the opportunity to ask Derek where I might find the music to go with the words. "Oh, what I've done is to set the words so we can use familiar tunes which fit," he said. "For instance, I thought that for that first chorus, 'Oh someone is coming to blow Mina up,' you'd be using the tune *The Bare Necessities*."

With nothing more interesting to watch on television that night when I got home than *Celebrity Places In The Sun From Hell*, I decided to see if I could set the chorus as suggested, with some harmonisation as well. I wasn't the least bit convinced by the fit of the tune with the words, but it was gone half past ten by the time I'd finished the first draft and, duly summoned by Katie to treat myself to some time back in the real world, I decided to turn in for the night.
I'd just got off to sleep when at ten past midnight the phone rang and I found myself speaking to Derek once more.
"I'm so sorry," he said. "I've just realised. It was *Hi Ho, Hi Ho, It's Home From Work We Go* for the first chorus. Remember that one? From Walt Disney's *Snow White and the Seven Dwarfs?"*
If it's a Disney theme he's after, I don't see why we can't just sing every single chorus to the tune *Supercalifragilisticexpialidocious*. Would certainly reduce photocopying time and costs. As well as my projected short-to-medium-term monthly diazepam dependency levels.

Sunday 21st September
An improvement in numbers at church this morning, although no great reduction in average age.
Over coffee afterwards, a genial-looking man whose fresh face suggested he had a part to play in keeping that average age the right side of 78 came up to me. "I am so looking forward to your Dolls House concert," he said. "I'm one of the patrons, you see. And member of the Dellford Rotary Club. If it goes well on Saturday, I'll be happy to put in a good word for you among some of my fellow Rotarians. Very influential body."
This certainly was very encouraging. "Thank you very much," I said politely. "We'll do our best to give you a super evening."
"I gather there were one or two slight hiccups in the arrangements," he went on.
"Oh, we got there in the end," I said unthinkingly, "no thanks to our new so-called events co-ordinator who nearly bodged the whole thing up."
"Betty Crabtree?" the man enquired.
I suddenly realised what I'd said. "Oh, crumbs, I'm so sorry," I said, conscious that my cheeks were now half a dozen shades pinker. "I always seem to put my foot in it when I darken the doors of this building. You'll probably turn round now and tell me she's your mother, won't you?"
"No," he replied. "She's my wife."

Monday 22nd September
The post today brought a long letter from Patience Drummond, the one who'd failed her voice test 12 days ago. I lost count of the number of times she used the words "irregularities" or "fatally flawed" which she

seemed to apply to every aspect of the voice test, from the temperature of the waiting room to the height of the table used by the voice testing panel. The most serious of our many shortcomings was, she maintained, our failure to properly articulate the precise reasons for rejecting her and failure to reduce these to written form including information on rights of appeal against the decision. One might have thought we'd just taken a decision to deport her and her family to a forced labour camp in southern Angola. She has asked for a meeting after our rehearsal on Wednesday evening when she expects sight of "all relevant documentation pertinent to the issue" and has said that if we refuse, she will "consider whether to take professional advice with a view to further action."

I remembered what Stan had said after we'd taken the decision at the voice test, and decided to seek his views. I didn't catch him at the best time: apparently Edna had just given him an ear-bashing after someone had left a mugful of coffee on a sideboard following last Wednesday's rehearsal and was threatening to "get physical" if it happened again. I sympathised with him, naturally, then asked him how seriously we should take Patience Drummond's implied threats.

"Well, the last time a decision in the village didn't go her way, she certainly ruffled a lot of feathers," he said. "It started as a complaint to an official. That apparently wasn't resolved to her satisfaction, so she made a formal written submission to the organisers. They wrote back but she wasn't happy with the reply so demanded a meeting. And at that meeting, she made allegations of negligence and demanded redress for psychological harm arising from it, and said if she did not receive a satisfactory settlement she would instruct solicitors with a view to proceedings in the civil courts."

"And what led to the original complaint?" I asked.

"Being adjudged not to have been first across the finishing line in the village sports egg and spoon race," said Stan.

Wednesday 24th September

Another super rehearsal tonight, but it was rather overshadowed by the prospect of a confrontation with Patience Drummond. I was so worried about it that I wondered if we should consider just letting her in and cutting our losses. But Alan was adamant. "Once she gets a foot in the door, she won't give us a moment's peace," he said. "I've come across barrack-room lawyers like this before."

He suggested we simply told her that we weren't bound by any constitution or procedural rules, nor were we obliged to be, and that we reiterated that her voice, while not bad, didn't come up to the standard expected by the group. He added, much to my relief, that he'd be happy to do the talking. But I noticed that even he looked ill at ease as, at the

appointed time, Patience Drummond strode in, sat down and from a Waitrose carrier bag produced an enormous lever arch file, bulging with papers.
"Before we get properly under way," she began, "may I ask if anybody is minuting this meeting?"
"We can certainly take a note of the main points," said Alan. "But I hardly…."
"I think it essential that we establish that a verbatim transcript can be made available before we commence any discussion on the various points I need to make," she said. She pointed to Stan, who I'd asked to stay in the room to give us some moral support. "May I ask who he is?"
"Stan Dewsnap," Stan replied. "I'm a member of the committee."
"Oh, now that is interesting," said Patience. "I wasn't aware the group had a committee as such. Before we start, I'd like to see a copy of the constitution and rules of the society."
"We haven't got one," said Alan. "We're a very informal, friendly group. We're not accountable to anybody."
"I'm sorry, but I don't accept that," said Patience. "Every group which invites participation from other people is accountable. I must insist that I be made aware of the availability of the rules under which you operate, the criteria for selection and appointment of committee members, protocols regarding the presence of society members for voice tests and appeals against those that are unsuccessful, and arrangements for the minuting and recording of meetings."
"That will all take some time," said Alan. No doubt hoping, like me, that in that time she'd have forgotten all about it.
"You've had since Monday," she said dangerously. "Am I going to see some documentation? Or are you simply making all this up as you go along?"
Alan sighed. Stan pursed his lips. I suddenly felt a compelling urge to be herding llamas in Surinam.
"Well?" Patience demanded.
At which point the door burst open to reveal Edna Mudge, brandishing a large coffee mug. Charging up to Stan with the sensitivity and decorum of a gorilla with toothache, she drew back the mug and unleashed its considerable contents all over his face. "I warned you!" she yelled, then stomped out the way she had come.
I glanced at Patience and saw she had turned quite white. Sensing the slenderest of opportunities, and seeking to drive home the advantage, I pointed in the direction taken by Edna. "If you do ever join us," I said, "I can tell you it's best not to upset her."
"Actually," said Patience, stuffing her lever arch file back in her Waitrose bag, "I am very busy over the next few months. I don't think I would

have had time to devote to this group in any event. Thank you and goodnight."

Alan and I waited till she was safely out of the building before heaving a joint sigh of inestimable relief. Stan stood there calmly, using his handkerchief to wipe the remaining coffee stains from his eyelids.

"Very careless of me to have left that mugful of cold coffee on the draining board," he mused. "Especially with Edna coming in tonight."

"You are a genius," I said gratefully. "I hope it wasn't too unpleasant having the stuff thrown in your face."

Stan permitted himself a grin. "I tell you," he said, "to get rid of Patience Drummond, I'd have been happy to have been drip fed the contents of the overflowing sewer behind Ali Dervisoglu's kebab shop in Horspool Road."

Saturday 27th September

Got a call from Betty Crabtree this morning. "I've had a call from Mrs Bassett, the organiser of tonight's concert," she said. "She says they're expecting eighteen people there and want to know if that's going to be a problem."

I considered. When we'd done Stainer's *Crucifixion* with the Wolverhampton Polytechnic Glee Club we'd had an audience of six nuns and a restless wasp, and last year we'd done a concert at St Basil's Church where because of an accident and resulting road closures very nearby we'd started with precisely three. It was disappointing, certainly, but eighteen was better than seventeen and if they were grouped round tables it wouldn't look too embarrassingly empty. I told Betty I was happy for us to go ahead.

We'd decided against an afternoon rehearsal but agreed to assemble in the curator's office at seven for a warm-up. When I arrived, I was surprised to see that the foyer was already quite full of people, so I made a beeline for Mrs Bassett and asked if there'd been a last minute upsurge in numbers.

"No, not to my knowledge," she said. "We actually had to turn people away when they enquired during the week."

"Turn people away?" I echoed. "How many are you expecting?"

"Eighty," she said. "I did ring this morning to ask if it would be a problem for the choir and I was told it wouldn't be."

Dazed, I tottered into the concert room and walked up the aisle, the width of which would certainly not have satisfied any health and safety inspectors who had nothing better to do with their Saturday nights. When I got to the end, I found that the tightly-packed rows of chairs stopped so that the front row stood no more than four feet from the far wall, in a

room that was hardly fifteen feet wide. There would barely be room for a size-zero soloist, yet alone a group of twenty singers.
Now in a state of near panic, I walked back out into the foyer and considered our options. Cancellation was out of the question: the punters were hobbling steadily in, accompanied by an assortment of mobility aids and already planning their quickest means of access to the powder rooms when their ageing bladders reached maximum tolerable levels. Performing with only a third of the membership would just make me look ridiculous and might alienate those I had to turn away. Placing Betty Crabtree in the village stocks and pelting her with rotten cabbages from Norman Snettisbury's ill-fated allotment would undoubtedly be hugely therapeutic but wouldn't address the problem and would simply create an additional logistical headache for me, namely that the village stocks were locked away in Dellford's town museum and next available for public viewing at ten on Monday morning. And setting up a video-linked facility enabling us to perform in the curator's room while the audience watched us on a specially installed wide flat-screen TV supported by speakers strategically placed throughout the exhibition hall might take slightly longer than the 25 minutes available and would place something of a strain on the concert budget of seventy-five pounds 50p.
"We've got no choice," I said. "We'll have to go ahead."
Somehow, amid much wailing, gnashing of teeth, and clashing of walking sticks, we managed to narrow the gaps between the rows of chairs to allow all the singers to squeeze into the space between the front row and the wall, and we got under way just ten minutes late. We were helped marginally by the fact that Marjorie, who had the potential to occupy space for two people, wasn't present, for reasons that weren't altogether clear, but at that moment it wouldn't have surprised me to have found that Betty Crabtree had told her the concert was being held tomorrow night at the Great Hall, Empire Club, Sandy Beach Caravan Park, Westward Ho! But my relief that we did not have that problem to contend with was wholly outweighed by my dismay when I observed that seated directly below me, once I had carved out my own territory – all three square millimetres of it – was a ruddy-faced old lady who even before we began singing appeared to wish she was somewhere else completely. And once we got going, all I seemed to be able to focus on was her heavy breathing, her audible sighing and her tutting when the length of a piece was not to her satisfaction, and, in response to Alan's witty and inventive linking speeches, a countenance that was stonier than the scree slopes on the north face of Ben Nevis.
"Who is that old boot?" I asked Alan during the half-time drinks, thankfully served to us in the curator's office.

"Try not to upset her," he said. "She's Daphne Venters, the founder of this place. And that's her husband Clifford sitting to her left. Bear in mind it's probably for her to decide how much the donation will be. Which we could use, believe you me."

And so to the second half. Excitement welled up inside me as I realised that we might actually get to perform a whole concert without being frustrated by coffee-stained pet animals, verbose appeals on behalf of potential suicides, and maverick Southdown double-deckers. But the sense of anticipation quickly dissolved into infuriating anticlimax. Somehow the chairs had been pushed forward again leaving us with, if anything, even less space than we'd had at the start of the evening, and the tutting and sighing from Daphne Venters was now being emitted for each piece that lasted longer than 40 seconds. And her husband was by now giving out equally negative signals. I tried to avoid the eyes of the other singers, but somehow I knew they, like me, were just willing the whole sorry business to end as quickly as possible, and it was a huge relief to embark on our last piece, our splendid *a cappella* version of Flanders & Swann's *Transport Of Delight*. As we reached the final, climactic lines, in my state of elation I seemed to forget myself, leaned forward, caught my foot on the oustretched shoe belonging to a somnolent octogenarian and was smartly catapulted into Clifford Venters' lap.

Still, we had somehow made it to the end of the concert. But if I thought that meant an early escape, I was to be very quickly disabused. As the applause, such as it was, died down, we were asked to remain where we were while Mrs Bassett stood up, thanked us for our hard work and then announced the raffle draw. With over 30 prizes. However, with the number of non-responses when numbers were called, or cries of "Put it back" when the owner of the winning ticket realised he or she had already won a prize, it must have been necessary to draw at least fifty tickets. Finally, mercifully, we got down to the last three prizes, but again, the same ghastly ritual of the number being called and no response. I turned to Alan and said "I'd swing for the owner of that wretched ticket" only to glance cursorily at the tickets I'd bought and realised it was mine.

But with the not inconsiderable forms of Clifford and Daphne Venters as well as half a dozen pairs of outstretched legs needing to be negotiated before I could access the prize table, and no immediate access to a magic carpet or a team of specialist tunnelling contractors, I decided to hold my peace. Especially with the choice of prizes now limited to a framed picture of Dellford Corn Exchange By Night, a hamster lover's pocket notebook and a gift-wrapped bottle of scented carpet shampoo.

OCTOBER

Wednesday 1st October

A rather subdued evening's rehearsal following last Saturday's events. Charlie was there, being rather more caustic and annoying than usual. The trio of girls calling themselves the Three Fivers didn't come, so we were rather depleted on the soprano line, and it showed as we began our work on our Christmas programmes. We agreed that it was good to have got through a concert for a change, but none of us had particularly enjoyed the experience. We cheered ourselves up by planning ahead for a possible tour in northern France next spring, including two or three concerts of English music, and we also felt it would be good to have proper uniforms and decent folders.

If we could afford it all, of course.

Derek told me the first rehearsal of his play was taking place tomorrow night and asked me if I'd like to come along. Notwithstanding my misgivings about the whole thing, I was anxious to support Derek in his new venture, and reflected that through my involvement, albeit fairly superficial, there might be the potential for more members of the singing group. Accordingly, I said I'd do it.

"Who are the actors?" I asked. "Are they in the Dellford drama group?"

"They're on the membership list, yes," said Derek. "And Alexander Duddleswell was in the last play."

I was slightly troubled by his reply, and my concerns were not allayed in the least when Charlie buttonholed me a few moments later.

"When he says they're on the membership list," he said, "he means they've not been chosen for a part in any of their plays for about the last ten years. For want of a better expression, they're the group's cast-offs."

"What about Alexander Duddleswell?" I enquired. "He was in the last play apparently."

"That's right," said Charlie. "And not likely to be in another one. Not after his entry onto the stage in Act 3 Scene 2."

"What about it?"

"He'd been murdered in Act 1 Scene 4," said Charlie.

Thursday 2nd October

Alan rang as I was about to go out tonight telling me Geraint had spoken to him to ask if some of us might be available to come to church on Sunday morning to do a Harvest-time piece that we'd popped into last weekend's reconstruction of West Ruislip up platform on a snowy Monday morning.

Bearing in mind that being a Harvest Festival there might be a reasonable number of visitors who in turn might be interested in joining us if they

heard how good we were, I jumped at the opportunity, and after a few phone calls had managed to secure eight voices for the service.
Then it was back to the Assembly Room, much to Katie's annoyance it has to be said, to see the first rehearsal of *The Strange Case Of The Exploding Christmas Puddings*.
Unfortunately, my optimism that the band of alleged actors on parade tonight might provide potential additional membership for my group was found to have been hopelessly misplaced. Derek announced that the work he was to be doing tonight involved five players, of whom three were unavailable through a mixture of illness and work commitments. It was certainly unfortunate that one of those three was the central character, Lady Wilhelmina (Mina to her friends) Muggleton of Muggleton Manor, sadly unavoidably detained by an attack of gallstones. That just left Derek himself, playing the part of the dastardly Doctor Douglas Rutherford who was strongly implicated in the first of a number of attempts on the life of Lady Wilhelmina, and Alexander Duddleswell, playing Eustace Rampisham the distinctly dodgy handyman, who was certainly present if not exactly correct. "I just love that first line," Alexander said to me. "Chester, Lady Wilhemina's youngest son, asks me 'Do you know what we're all on this earth for, Rampisham?' and I reply 'You hum it, Master Chester, and I'll play it!' Great, that, isn't it. You hum it and I'll play it! Reminds me of those monkeys on the BP Tips tea adverts!"
My sides were in no immediate danger of splitting on the first hearing of this supposedly hilarious opening to the play, but there were certainly other parts of me that were coming very close to breaking point as Derek painstakingly went over this particular exchange a good half dozen times – unable, apparently, to conclude whether the handyman should adopt an English, Indian, Japanese or Spanish nationality. Not that, when Alexander tried the various accents, I could tell a blind bit of difference between any of them.
I was about to make my excuses, give up the evening as a bad job and surprise Katie by returning early, when Derek asked me if I would in fact fill in as Lady Wilhemina while he played Chester and Lord Muggleton. I was assured that although I had quite a few lines, all I had to do by way of acting was to sit inscrutably at the table and pretend, at the key moment at the end of the scene, to take a bite out of a Christmas pudding. Derek, anxious as he put it "to get cast members working with their props as quickly as possible," was kind enough to supply me with a piece of screwed-up paper and asked me to bite into that.
I noticed that as I got to my "bite moment," some two and a half ghastly hours later, Derek had crept round behind me, but thought nothing of it until, after I had delivered the immortal line "A very perceptive piece of pudding, Dr Rutherford" – I can see the editors of the *Oxford Dictionary*

Of Quotations adding it to their database already – and placed the screwed up paper back on the table, there was the most deafening blast from behind me. I started so violently that I shot forward and crashed out of my chair onto the ground.
"Well done," said Derek, holding up the used-up remains of a pink balloon towards my prostrate frame. "Do you know that is just the reaction I wanted?"
"You hum it, Mr Prodoocer, and I'll play it!" chortled Alexander and the two men distintegrated into paroxysms of laughter.
Got home just as Katie was disposing of the congealed sludge that an hour and a half ago would have been my appetising dinner. "And your cup of tea will probably be cold by now," she added.
At least it wasn't BP Tips.

Sunday 5th October
To church this morning for the Harvest service.
We agreed that we would sing our seasonal ditty immediately after the various offerings of food were brought up to the altar to be blessed and then transferred to the back of the church for conveyance to the elderly and infirm of the parish. Although as most of them were in church already, I'm not sure why we couldn't just have invited them to help themselves. Katie and I had brought a large basket of appetising-looking fruit and vegetables, purchased from Green's delicatessen in town, including some enormous tomatoes. Possibly too large a basket, for as I looked out at the congregation on my way back from the altar to check that I had my complement of singers, my hand slipped, the basket slipped with it, and a number of pieces of fruit sitting on top of the basket slid off, with a particularly large pineapple dropping straight into the lap of Daphne Venters. I was disappointed she chose to take it so ungraciously. In every sense.
Moments later we took our places for the eagerly-awaited choral item. I stepped forward confidently to announce to the congregation what the piece was to be, only to find my foot descending onto something that was definitely not the stone church floor. The hideous sensation of a Doc Marten size eleven making contact with what first seemed like rubber and then mush confirmed that I had just stepped on possibly the largest tomato ever to grace the aisle of St Augustine of Hippo's. And no prizes for guessing into whose lap the juice went.
It was hardly surprising that the subsequent performance, during the whole of which I was conscious that my face was as red as the fruit I had just squashed, and conscious too of smirks on the faces of every member of the congregation who'd just witnessed my *faux pas*, lacked any real conviction and wasn't the greatest piece of PR we had ever mounted.

"Still," said Alan. "Could have been worse. We might have chosen 'You say tomayto, I say tomarto.'"
Except I wish we had called the whole thing off.

Tuesday 7th October

A very disappointing day today. After receiving a letter from the Dolls House Exhibition enclosing a cheque which was indeed considerably less than what we'd hoped for, I got a phone call from Alan to say there was a message on his answering machine from Kirsty on behalf of the Three Fivers.
"I wrote her message down word for word," he said. "'Last Saturday's concert I get there right and I'm like I so am not wanting to be here and Betty Crabtree's like well you've not got a proper folder and I'm like er hallo what are you on and she gives me you know this totally gross brown paper folder and she's like you've got to have this one and I'm like er excuse me shall I just go home and then she's on at me about my make-up and going like you've put too much lippy on and I'm like ohhhh myyyyy God this woman is mental so I turn around and go yeah whatever and I'm like do I want to be in this place and us three we talked about it after and we're all just like we can't be bovvered anymore.'"
"So what are they saying?" I enquired.
"It means they're out of the group, I'm afraid," Alan replied. "I'll send you the bill in due course, shall I?"
"What for?" I queried.
"Translator's fees," said Alan.

Wednesday 8th October

Called an emergency committee meeting following our rehearsal tonight. To my surprise, not only Charlie Tompkins but Angus Spadgwick and even Jonathan Perfrement turned up. We agreed that the priority was getting more members in but we also needed more money in the bank. Otherwise, as Charlie kept saying, we were never going to move forward as a choir. A fundraising and recruitment event of some kind during November was absolutely imperative.
"What about a bring and buy?" Alan said.
"Boring," said Charlie. "Complete turn-off."
"Any other suggestions then?" said Alan.
"Could do another concert with raffle, possibly away from here," said Mark.
"There's no time," said Alan. "We've already got enough to work towards as it is. What do you think, Jonathan?"
"I'd like to suggest a workshop," said Jonathan Perfrement. "We get away from our normal workplaces and gather in a neutral location. Good

quality face time, celebrating our strengths as a homogeneous unit. Standard Chatham House rules apply. Led by a duly elected change champion, we form, storm, norm and perform. No hogging or ducking, but a high-level thought shower, getting our ducks in a row, not being afraid to think outside the box and shoot the puppy. Start with a brain dump and bring to the meeting whatever ideas we have, recognising we're on a steep learning curve, drill them down to written format consisting of a schedule of bullets, achieve buy-in from all the stakeholders, then formulate and from there develop a targeted staged progression plan ratcheting up the need for application of finer detail based on the broad overall principles."
"All right, bring and buy it is," said Charlie.

Sunday 12th October
As Katie had gone to stay with some old college friends this weekend, I took the opportunity to invite the singers and the committee round for a buffet lunch. It was a very warm cloudless October day, and we were able to sit and enjoy our food outside.
"This great weather's given me an idea," said Frank Crotty, tucking into his second helping of strawberry Pavlova. "For the bring and buy sale in November, why don't we have a summer theme."
I gently pointed out to him that with Christmas approaching, a Yuletide theme would be more appropriate.
"That's just it," said Frank. "Too predictable. It'll be probably really cold or wet outside. People will be going to loads of other Christmas events in November and December. Yes, we can advertise it as a Christmas fayre, but we can cheer everyone up with lots of reminders of summer. Barbecue food, a big indoor sandpit for the children, candyfloss stall, background music conveying the idea of shimmering sands and waves lapping the shores....families will love it, particularly if it's a miserable day and summer holidays seem years away. Trust me. I'm more than happy to project manage this."
"This isn't the flipping *Apprentice*," Charlie pointed out, picking up his bowl and emptying the last drops of his fruit salad syrup into his mouth. "I mean, where do the singers come in? This is supposed to be a means of attracting new blood. Allegedly."
"I've got ideas for that too," said Frank. "We provide some singing and inject some summery atmosphere into our music and our outfits."
"As long as you're not suggesting we all stand up there singing Mungo Jerry's *In The Summertime* or Terry Dactyl And The Dinosaurs' *Seaside Shuffle* dressed in nothing but luminous swimming costumes," said Mike, helping himself to a slab of mature Cheddar.

"I've checked the Internet and there's a company that can provide a consignment of spotty pink bathing costumes within 24 hours," said Frank.
And I thought Geraint was the only one among us with a screw loose.
Angus sipped his coffee meditatively. "It does occur to me," he said, "that we could attract more people to a bring and buy if I were to do a sexed-out plug for it in my column."
"Sexed-up," said Charlie, "and if we're honest, my dear Agnes, the chances of anybody feeling sexed up by reading anything in your column are about as great as a bag of McDonalds French fries having made contact with a potato."
"Now, there you're wrong," said Angus. "Remember that spring fayre at our church a few years back where I promised a guest appearance by Cliff Richard and Rod Stewart and the chance to win a prize of half a million pounds in cash? We packed the place out. They all fell for it. My best April Fool column joke ever."
"Except," said Charlie, "you'll recall there was an unusually large number of deaths that week. Or used cars for sale. One of those. And your column had to be moved."
"Where to?" I enquired.
"May the thirteenth," said Charlie.

Tuesday 14th October

As I had the rare luxury of a proper lunch break today, I decided to visit the Dellford Music Supplies store to see what they had by way of music on a summer theme and less frequently performed Christmas carols. Alan and I agreed that it'd be nice to do something a bit different and we'd put together a list of some songs we knew vaguely that we thought would be fun to do. I arrived at the shop and my attention was immediately drawn to a notice in the window – THIS IS A FAMILY STORE, OWNED LOCALLY. Next to it was another, smaller notice encouraging us to SHOP LOCALLY, SUPPORT LOCAL BUSINESS AND STEM THE TIDE OF INTERNET SHOPPING WHICH THREATENS TO SWAMP OUR HIGH STREETS WITH BLAND CHAIN STORES AND DOWDY CHARITY SHOPS.
Happy to do my bit of tide-stemming, I went in to find the shop completely changed from when I had last visited. Most of the floor space was now taken over by instruments and other paraphernalia one might expect in a pop band, including guitars, keyboards, drumkits and amplifiers, and instead of soothing classical background music I found myself suffering an earful of Status Quo. I made my way to the counter and asked the gentleman there if he could direct me to the choral sheet music.

“We’ve not got a lot in at the moment,” he said, indicating an area of shelving behind him less than six inches long, a goodly portion of which was occupied by the score of Handel’s *Messiah* . He took a look at the list I had with me and shook his head sadly. “To be honest,” he said, “for this sort of thing, your best bet’s the Internet.”
I pointed out to him that I was trying to buck the trend towards Internet shopping by supporting local business, as directed by the sign outside.
“I know,” he said, “but we’re entirely in the hands of head office that buys in our stock.”
“Head office?” I echoed. “What about your sign? You know, Owned Locally?”
“Oh, I’ve been meaning to take that down,” the man on the counter informed me. “We were taken over last week. Sadly, head office is no longer upstairs.”
“Where is it?” I enquired. “Salisbury, or Bournemouth, maybe?” ”Denver, Colorado,” he replied.

Friday 17th October
Following an excellent meeting on Wednesday, I suddenly feel a lot more optimistic about the immediate future of our group. We’ve not only decided that we will do some busking for the High Sheriff, the date for which has now been confirmed as 12th December, but we have confirmed dates for our pre-Christmas carol concerts, one in the Assembly Room and one in church, and have also agreed to provide a choir for the midnight service on Christmas Eve.
And there was a positive development on the music-hunting front today. After explaining to the group on Wednesday evening how hard it was to find new and interesting music on a limited budget, I had a call this morning from Mike. He told me that an old customer of his, Molly Gorple, had a huge quantity of music, some of it potentially quite valuable, and he suggested I might like to have a look at it. I called her straightaway and she invited me to pop round whenever convenient; as it happened, I had a free couple of hours so cycled straight back to Hobden Crescent, one of the leafier parts of Lambsball Green, to see her. She was a delightful lady, providing me with a cup of tea and a slice of really delicious chocolate cake, and produced a large green bag, presumably intended for the disposal of gardening waste, containing a vast amount of sheet music.
“You can help me if you like,” she said. “I used to collect first editions and original autographed copies of musical works. It’s all in here, together with other stuff I’ve collected through the years. Of course a lot of it’s rubbish. I’d put little yellow labels on all the good stuff for when I got round to cataloguing it. But then my arthritis set in and I couldn’t, and

to make matters worse my daughter was over the other week and when she was tidying for me she mixed it all up. If you could separate the yellow label stuff and take out anything else you like the look of, then throw the rest away, I'd be so grateful."
"If you trust me with the yellow label stuff, I'll catalogue it for you if you want," I said.
"I think that's worth another slice of chocolate cake!" Molly beamed.
With a halo more lustrous, but with a waistline considerably more substantial, than twenty minutes previously, I got down to work in her front room. It was true that a lot of the material was either cheesier than a piece of Caerphilly stuck in a marathon runner's left trainer, or sicklier than the rum babas I used to munch in the Wimpy bar on Walsall High Street on a Saturday morning. But there was certainly plenty of music which I thought we could attempt, and although I'm no expert, it's clear that her so-called yellow-label material was potentially very valuable indeed. I placed the good and valuable music in my stout carrier bag I'd brought for the purpose, and put the Caerphilly-and-rum-baba material back in the garden sack.
As I was nearing completion of the task, a short balding man appeared in the doorway. "Anything I can do for you today, Moll?" he asked. "Don't forget the recycling people come today. Do you want me to collect your waste paper and put it in my wheelie bin for you?"
"I don't think so, Mr Griggs," said Molly. "Not today."
I saw how I thought I could help. "I'll have a whole load of waste paper in a few minutes," I said. "I'll leave it in the green bag just outside."
"That's fine," said Mr Griggs. "I'll be back shortly."
With the deposit of *When I Sucked Ambrosian Juice* by Dr Elwyn Codrington and *Can I Count On Kissing You Tonight* by Elliot J Schwarzenhopfer IV into the garden sack, the job was finally done, and I ceremoniously threw the receptacle in question onto the gravel driveway outside, at the same time placing my carrier bag carefully in the porch.
"There we are," I said to Molly. "Job done."
"Another slice of chocolate cake?" Molly responded. Although a more unMafia-like soul it would be hard to imagine, her offer was one I really couldn't refuse, and when I got up from the table twenty minutes later, with only a small wedge left on the plate to show for what had been a truly colossal chocolatey culinary creation, I was seriously concerned as to whether my bicycle would support the additional poundage of sugar and buttercream icing, mixed in with Lambsball Green's entire supply of Cadbury's Dairy Milk. I looked out to see the recycling lorry moving away down the road; a glance at the empty gravel driveway told me the musical dross that had hitherto been cluttering Molly's abode, *inter alia*

the lesser works of Elwyn Codrington and Elliot J Schwarzenhopfer IV, had gone with it.
I bent down to retrieve my carrier bag and to my surprise saw no bag there at all. I was about to ask Molly if she'd moved it when Mr Griggs hove back into view clutching the bag which looked horribly empty.
"Just got them in time," he said. "They almost beat me to it. It was the green bag you said you wanted emptying, wasn't it?"
"Yes," I said. "The big green gardening bag I left on the driveway."
"I didn't see a big green gardening bag," said Mr Griggs. "Dustmen must have taken that themselves. I just saw this carrier bag with GREEN on it." And he produced the bag Katie and I had been given from Green's delicatessen a fortnight ago when buying our Harvest hamper.
Notwithstanding a madcap dash round every street in Lambsball Green, a series of phone calls to the council offices who found every conceivable reason – from end-of-week staff shortages to the failure of the kidney bean crop in Trinidad and Tobago – not to disclose the likely destination of recyclable material culled from Hobden Crescent, and a heart-stopping 70mph tour of all the locality's recycling depots in Mr Griggs' rust-riddled 1983 Volkswagen Polo, all efforts to trace the music in question ended in abject failure.
To give him credit when we finally returned two hours later, Mr Griggs was kind enough to break the bad news to Molly and accept his share of the blame, pacifying her to the extent that she felt able to offer me a soothing cup of tea. A cup of tea being about as much as I felt able to stomach, with certainly neither the inclination nor the ability, for the foreseeable future, to ingest any further chocolate cake. Let alone suck any of Dr Codrington's Ambrosian juice.

Sunday 19th October

Geraint asked me to read the second lesson in church this morning. It was from the book of James, all on the theme of "faith without works is dead." I thought I had read it rather well, with a steady but not too fast pace and plenty of expression and conviction. Geraint, who can preach a pretty good sermon – provided he's not asked to mention by name any public figures born after about 1965, that is – spoke particularly well on the reading, using one of the verses I'd read as his text. After the service I thought it would be nice to give him what Jonathan Perfrement might call "positive feedback." I rather suspect poor Geraint doesn't get too much of that.
"Really good sermon," I said to him. "And I was so pleased that you based it on what I'd read."

"I'm glad to hear it," said Geraint, "especially when I thought I was going to be preaching about turning water into wine. From the reading you were supposed to be doing."
Not for the first time at St Augustine's, I found myself hoping I was standing on a trapdoor and there was poised a kindly minion who would pull a lever and summarily despatch me thirty feet into a vat of boiling Branston Pickle. "I am so sorry," I said.
"I shouldn't worry," said Geraint. "Be prepared, as Mr Simpkins my old scoutmaster said. Besides, perhaps the good Lord was trying to tell us both something."
"How do you mean?" I asked.
"I had a phone call from Betty Crabtree on Friday," said Geraint. "She was asking whether she'd done anything to upset you. The Singers seem to have got quite a lot of events planned for the rest of the year and you've not asked her to help out at any of them."
I couldn't help thinking back to her shambolic performance in relation to the Dolls House Exhibition concert which had resulted in our nearly failing to turn up at all, the loss of three of our strongest sopranos, and our coming within an ace of being packaged up by John West and placed on the tinned sardine shelves in the Dellford Tesco Express. "To be honest," I said, "her track record so far hasn't been brilliant."
"Sometimes, David," said Geraint quietly, "we have to learn to forgive, and place compassion and sympathy for the needs of the disadvantaged before our own selfish aspirations. I'll leave it with you."
Katie and I discussed it later. We agreed that the plan has always been to create a community organisation; to exclude those whom we have welcomed amongst us and who have given up their time to help that organisation is insensitive and uncaring, and we must strive to engage positively with even the more challenging elements within it in order not to compromise our underlying objectives.
Which isn't to say that I can trust Betty Crabtree to ensure that for the next concert we organise in Lambsball Green we are all in the same place at the same time. I suspect that compassion and sympathy for the needs of the disadvantaged will be in somewhat short supply if while the singers are waiting in the church the audience are down the pub, the music is in a barge drifting down the Thames Estuary, and the refreshments are in the staff locker room of the Quick Fix DIY Warehouse in Gasworks Lane Industrial Estate, Warrington.

Wednesday 22nd October

A busy and productive evening. An excellent rehearsal, although the weakness on the soprano line without the Three Fivers was very obvious,

and then some serious planning for what we are calling the Christmas Summer Fayre, to take place on Saturday 15th November.
We decided that there will be a mixture of Yuletide and seaside stalls, with Karen and Susan taking responsibility for the Christmas aspect and Frank the summery part of the proceedings. Karen and Susan really have the easier part: the two of them plus Jim, Mike, Jack and Gail will look after the Christmas gifts and seasonal produce, and already Elphine has undertaken to make two and a half thousand mince pies and a cake the size of which it is hoped will interest the *Guinness Book Of Records*. The rest of the group except Alan, Geraint(who has wisely decided not to get involved) and myself will oversee the seaside attractions including the sandpit, barbecue, jellied eels store, and, providing Dobbin's fetlock passes a late fitness test, pony rides round the immediate streets and fields. It was also suggested we might engage a celebrity lookalike to come and be photographed beside customers with a make-believe background of golden sands and tropical palms. We agreed it would be great to invite the press there too, to generate even more publicity for our group.
There was only one thing that unsettled me. "What about Betty Crabtree?" I asked, recalling my conversation with Geraint on Sunday. "What can we give her to do?"
"A load of balls," said Frank.
There was a gasp-ette from the others.
"I mean she can sell beach balls," Frank said. "Not just beach balls. Footballs, tennis balls – all the sorts of balls you might find on a beach. I've got contacts with wholesale suppliers of those too. Very popular and great fun."
We all agreed that the margin for balls-ups with balls sales was sufficiently narrow to allow Betty to be assigned this task, and moved on.
"What about the bathing costumes?" Gail enquired. "Are we still up for that?"
"Definitely," said Frank. "I'm not suggesting we stay in our gear all day. Just for the singing slots we do."
"Timed, presumably, to ensure the central heating in the Assembly Room has kicked in first," said Jack.
"Well, I think it'll be fun," said Gail. And from the various nods and murmurs of assent around the room, it seemed that most agreed with her.
"And we really think this will be effective in getting us new members?" Jim put in.
"I think there's every chance," said Frank.
About as much chance, I fear, as a pot-bellied porker flying past the Assembly Room and dropping through the window a piece of paper

bearing the winning numbers for next week's £18 million rollover lottery jackpot.
Did some googling tonight to endeavour to find a local celebrity lookalike. It seemed that according to the Web, unless we wanted to venture outside a radius of 40 miles, we'd have a straight choice between Ronnie Corbett and Ronnie Corbett. I was about to give it up as a bad job, but decided on the off-chance to check the local paper....which revealed an ad inserted by an Alice Templeton of Dellford who claimed to be a lookalike for Amy Winehouse. Accordingly I decided to give her a try, regarding the loss of the crucial last 5 minutes of a repeat of *Relocation Relocation* as a sacrifice worth making. Her line was constantly engaged for the next hour, but, at the additional cost of some much-needed sleep, I managed to get her household at just before eleven. A woman who sounded distinctly middle-aged answered the phone.
"Is that Alice Templeton?" I asked.
"I'm afraid she's gone to bed," she said. "This is Nerys, her daughter. I'm staying with her for a day or two."
This certainly did throw me. "Well," I said rather uncertainly. "I'm ringing about the celebrity lookalike thing."
"Oh, yes," said Nerys. "She's always been a hero of my mum's."
Considering Miss Winehouse herself had probably been alive for barely a third of the time of Alice Templeton, I thought this a surprising statement. Somewhat diffidently I replied "Er – if you don't mind my saying, she seems a little on the old side to be imitating this lady."
"Possibly," said Nerys. "But you can't deny this lady, as you put it, is an icon. Or national treasure to quote the current vernacular. She's taken more than her fair share of criticism for what she's done, but she's always been true to herself and we need more of her type around today. If we did, there wouldn't be so much misbehaviour amongst the young. And my mum's really done her homework on her. She's got the wig, the glasses, the handbag and the sensible tweeds."
This certainly didn't sound like the latest pop superstar. "I see," I said.
"Yes," Nerys went on. "She's certainly the most convincing Mary Whitehouse you'll ever see."

Friday 24th October
Rhiann rang to ask if I'd like to pop down to the pub for an early drink this evening to meet her friend Harvey Rutter who she said "is the spitting image" of a certain film star and absolutely perfect for the celebrity lookalike role we have in mind, before they go off together to meet friends in town. I said I'd be delighted.
I was about to go down to the Welldiggers when Betty Crabtree phoned, saying Geraint had told her I might be in touch with her about her

contribution to the fayre. I said that as I was going down to the Welldiggers, why didn't she join me later after Rhiann and Harvey had gone.
When I arrived, I couldn't believe it. The likeness between Harvey and Leonardo di Caprio was absolutely astonishing, and I saw a lot of customers looking in his direction obviously wondering if it really was him. He was a lovely guy; he said he'd be delighted to do it and would require no payment other than regular beers throughout the day, and added that if ever we needed our takings boosted by similar events in future, he was only a mobile phone call away.
Off he and Rhiann went to paint Dellford red, if such a thing were possible, and it was then just a case of waiting for Betty. She appeared in due course, looking rather ruddy in the face and certainly more exuberant than I think I'd ever seen her. I talked through what I had in mind for her, namely the sale of a collection of spherical objects. No gimmicks and no complicated arrangements or arithmetic, but just standing by a big binful of the things, taking money when it was offered. Not even Betty, I was sure, could go wrong with that.
"Yes, that all seems fine," she said. "Just selling balls from my bin." "By George, I think you've got it," I said, conscious of feeling as well as sounding a bit like Henry Higgins on hearing Eliza Doolittle advising him as to the rarity of hurricanes in Hertfordshire. I felt ever so slightly proud of myself not only for having done my Christian duty but having also found a way of engaging with Betty's brain cells. Maybe she was a bit more switched on than I'd given her credit for.
"By the way," I said, "you seem very excited about something." "Oh yes," she said. "On my way in I met one of my all-time favourite film stars talking to Rhiann, you know, from your group. I told him I've seen all his films. I'm one of his greatest fans. I'm usually hopeless at recognising celebrities as well."
I smiled at her indulgently. "Well recognised this time anyway," I said.
"I even asked him for his autograph," Betty said, producing a rather grubby old bus ticket from her bag. "And he gave it to me. Look, here it is. Harry Potter."

Sunday 26th October

On my way into church this morning I met Frank Crotty clutching a carrier bag. "Great news," he cried exultantly. "Geraint's away and the man who's taking the service has agreed I can make an announcement about the Christmas summer fayre."
I told him I was pleased to hear it but it was hardly up there with victory over Nazi Germany and the collapse of the Soviet Union as a development of earth-shattering significance.

"I've not told you the best bit," he said. "I'm going to dress up in my swimming costume to do it."
I somehow refrained from pointing out that we were endeavouring to attract punters to the fayre rather than put them off, and although I had no means of knowing what delights may present themselves when Frank removed his brown shirt, beige cardigan and grey trousers to reveal his middle-aged body, I wasn't convinced they would encourage those agonising over how to spend the middle Saturday in November to forsake racing from Redcar or one-day-only discounts in PC World.
Still, I could only admire his pluck, and I have to say that although I could barely watch it at first – in terms of charisma and sex appeal he was more George Formby than George Clooney, and I'd seen better dressed meat in the window of the Happy Butcher in Plunkett Street – he actually pulled it off pretty well and generated a few smiles from the hitherto poker-faced ranks of the faithful.
"Different, I suppose," the man sitting next to me said as the plug came to an end, Frank exited stage right, the tittering died down and the congregation resumed their own interpretation of the psalmist's instruction to be joyful in the Lord.
"Yes," I said. "I've not cringed as much in a service since at my last church we had an outreach service and there was an act from some drag queen. Never seen anything so awful. Over made-up, huge false boobs, bushy armpits, fishnet tights which completely failed to mask the hairy legs….not so much outreach as upchuck. You get the idea?"
"Frequently," he replied. "She is my sister, after all."

Tuesday 28th October

Two annoying developments today in relation to the planning of the fayre. The first was a call from Angus Spadgwick telling me that not only is the editor of the paper not prepared to do a special feature on our fayre in the news pages – the best apparently we can expect is a cameraman and reporter turning up on the day, providing they get decent notice of the arrangements – but Angus himself is going to have to devote fewer inches of his own column to the fayre than he had planned. "Something more important's come up," he explained.
Even though Charlie's probably right that there's more life in, and significantly more reader interest generated by, the deaths section immediately to the right of Angus' column, I didn't like the thought of our publicity suffering and felt I could be forgiven for being less than charitable in response.
"Let me guess," I replied. "A plan to build a ten-lane motorway right through the middle of the village? A lorry smash on Seymour Walk

resulting in the spillage of highly toxic waste? Someone from the Brumby Estate winning five hundred grand on *Who Wants To Be A Millionaire*?"
"It's the council's plan to remove the waste bin outside number 28 Park Road," said Angus. "And re-site it outside number 37."
"I'd better let you go then, hadn't I," I said irritably. "So you can get on with ringing the nationals."
Then following a call from Gail saying a number of her friends love the idea of the fayre as long as there's plenty of nice traditional seafood – to quote her, "the jellier the eels, the better" – I was then rung by Mark to say he's been let down by his whelk salesman and we may have to scrub that aspect of the fayre altogether.
And as if those two setbacks weren't enough, the post brought a letter from the treasurer of the Lambsball Green Dippers saying my half-yearly subscription was overdue and advising of the Dippers' traditional sanction for non-payment. The letter bore a mobile phone contact number but no address.
Buoyed up by the pleasant prospect of a week's break with Katie's parents in their new home in Cumbria, I didn't object too much to spending half the evening on the phone trying to get through to one Lucas Netherfield, the sender of the subscription reminder, to ask where to send my money. The time spent listening to the engaged signal was, however, not completely wasted, as it occurred to me that his organisation, to the coffers of which I was about to add a further generous supplement, might be able to assist with providing marine refreshment for the fayre. At long last I did manage to speak to him and, having arranged where to send the outstanding amount, I was assured that there should be no problem in one of the members being available to obtain and sell seafood for us a fortnight on Saturday. They wanted paying a lot more than Mark's contact, which was a blow. Then again, I reflected, the Dippers was an unusual and vibrant organisation which provided entertainment and enjoyment for many people. Granted, I didn't particularly warm to the prospect of the Dippers' Christmas dinner and the "bit of fun afterwards" which knowing them could have been anything from giant squid wrestling to diving into a pool of shark-infested liquid cow dung. But the possibility of new members for our group from amongst their number remained, and it would indeed be churlish and short-sighted to cease to support a quirky contribution to the fabric of our community and a refreshing antidote to the anodyne and often dreary orthodoxies of so much of contemporary life.
And I didn't exactly relish the prospect of a dead halibut being shoved through my letter box.

NOVEMBER

Wednesday 12th November

Refreshed by a very necessary week away, arrived at tonight's rehearsal eagerly anticipating a positive progress report from our esteemed project manager on Saturday's fayre.

"It's all going very well," he said, although there was something in the way he said it that made me feel vaguely uneasy. "Sadly Dobbin the pony sustained a knee injury in training and his manager says he can't risk him. But we've got confirmation from the Dippers that they're providing the jellied eels and whelks etcetera, we've bagsful of really nice presents for the Christmas gift stalls, we've a silent auction for a giant Christmas cake, Leonardo di Caprio's had a special makeover, the swimming costumes arrived yesterday, and Elphine's made not only a vast amount of cakes and slices but enough chocolate log to feed the entire population of Mexico City."

"Great," I said. "Any problems?"

"There is one little difficulty," he said, "and that's over the press. They've got other things that afternoon and the best they can give us is a ten-minute slot, 4.50 to 5pm. Just as we're due to shut."

This was a real blow. We'd agreed that despite our initial reservations it would not only be desirable but essential, in the interests of publicising ourselves and our group, to be photo'ed in our beach gear and the last thing I wanted, having done our "slots" much earlier in the day, was for us all to have to put our costumes back on again at a time when we're busy trying to sell off the remaining stock, count the takings and persuade the stragglers to relieve themselves of their remaining loose change in return for half a hundredweight of unused Bakewell tarts.

"I thought we agreed before I left that you'd ring and sort out a cameraman and reporter at the time we wanted them," I said irritably.

"I'm sorry," said Frank, "but I hadn't reckoned on Betty Crabtree mixing the digits of the phone number up. And spending the entire period of your absence trying to get through to the features editor of the *Dellford And District Ferret Breeders' Quarterly*."

Thursday 13th November

Rang the *Dellford Chronicle* first thing to see if there was any way they could send their reporter and photographer to us at 3pm on Saturday, when our second singing slot was due to take place. Having been told by a recorded message that my call was important to them, I was then told it was in a queue; eventually I did get to speak to an actual person and patiently explained the reason for my call, only to be told "The line's busy, do you wish to hold?" and then for the next 10 minutes, "the line's still busy, do you still wish to hold?" I was eventually put through to the reporters' office and went through my entire spiel again, to be rewarded with the no more helpful and indeed infinitely more infuriating "I'll just see if there's anyone who can help you." There followed ten more minutes of absolute silence before the same voice told me "There's no-one around at the minute. Can I take a message and get someone to call you back?" Figuring that the chances of being called back were about as great as being rung by the senior elder of the Mormon Tabernacle Church in Philadelphia with a request to give the keynote speech at their forthcoming Women's Convention on the subject of 18th century techniques for gherkin bottling, I decided to visit the *Chronicle* offices in person. In the hope that there was someone within the layers of obstructive administration who actually wrote newspapers.

Miraculously I was told I could be seen very shortly by the reporters' secretary who assigned reporters to particular events. I was duly ushered into the holy of holies and having been introduced to a Sarah Welling I found myself explaining my problem for the third time that morning.

Having listened to what I had to say, she went to her computer and keyed in the details. "You'll have to forgive me," she said. I wasn't sure I necessarily agreed with that. "We've only just installed the technology and we're having a few teething problems." However the ability of the machine in front of her to push through its incisors and molars seemed to be the least of its worries as a succession of painful electronic noises was heard to come from somewhere within its digestive system. After much key-tapping and even more gruesome bleeps, she was moved to announce "I'm sorry. It's just not letting me change the time." But that didn't stop her continuing to pore over the screen, muttering at irregular intervals "No, it's just not letting me....it won't let me.....I can't understand why it won't let me....it's never not let me before..." until she began to sound less like a level-headed competent businesswoman than a spoilt child at the zoo complaining about her mother's refusal to allow her to buy a plastic miniature elephant in the souvenir shop.

I wasn't sure whether after the eighth or perhaps ninth similar pronouncement I was expected to say "Oh well never mind, thanks for trying anyway" or condemn her to spend the rest of the decade in grim negotiation with a piece of hardware that possessed the reasonableness and malleability of a pit bull terrier. But mindful of the fact that I had a meeting to get back to in the year 2017, I put her out of her misery by telling her to forget it, and left, forced to speculate whether the reason for the computer's intransigence was down to her lack of IT literacy or a genuine clash with events the computer regarded as far more important. Which could have been anything from the Dellford Lapdancing Association's Topless Afternoon Tea Party to the play-off for promotion into the second tier of the North-West Iceland Ladies' Tiddlywinks Federation.

Saturday 15th November

The day of the fayre got off to a bad start. We'd arranged to go in at ten to set up and I was relaxing over a bowl of muesli at around nine thirty, learning that a belt of freezing Arctic weather had dropped much further south down the country than previously expected and wintry showers could therefore not be ruled out, when the phone rang. It was Alan.

"Stan's told me he can't be there this afternoon," he said. "He's out bowling. Which means I've got responsibility for the keys, the caretaking, the lot. One step out of place and it's the Mudge hit squad round to me with the poisoned umbrella."

"But I thought Stan said he'd cancel his bowling," I said, wiping a maverick raisin from my cheek.

"He had," said Alan. "But Betty Crabtree apparently asked him to get up there for eight o'clock to help her do a sign for her ball stall. No sign of her, he waited till nine then went round to see her and she told him she'd been waiting for him at eight last night. Called him an ignorant old fool. He quite reasonably decided to take his business elsewhere."

"Charming," I remarked.

"Yes," said Alan. "He was quite prepared to accept he was ignorant and a fool. It was the old he had the problem with."

To his credit, though, Stan did at least agree to be around for the setting-up during the morning, and with all the stallholders there promptly, and Leonardo di Caprio kindly lending a hand too, we found ourselves ready in good time for our gala opening at one o'clock.

All went splendidly right up until after four. The time sped past, business was brisk and everyone seemed to be enjoying themselves. Leonardo was as expected the most popular attraction, but the goodies provided by Elphine and the Dippers positively flew off the stalls – nobody had any idea that jellied eels and rock buns went so well together – and only a small amount of sand from the sandpit found its way into the sandwiches. Although it was a shame that shortage of manpower forced us to shut down most of our stalls to enable us to sing our two bathing-trunks selections, it was so warm in the Assembly Room that despite freezing cold temperatures outside there was no immediate danger of hypothermia inside. The best news of all was that as a result of our musical gimmickry, we attracted serious interest from at least a dozen people in becoming members of our group.

The only stall which wasn't doing great business was Betty's. With snow looming, one could perhaps understand the reluctance of potential customers to invest in beach and cricket balls. But more to the point, I couldn't believe potential punters would feel encouraged by the stallholder's seemingly permanently glazed expression, making me wonder if mentally she was actually with us at all, and not sunning herself on a golden Corfu beach or manning a marine aggregate dredger off Lossiemouth. So around four o'clock, to encourage a few more sales I suggested some fairly generous discounts for bulk purchase.

Within minutes my mini-ploy appeared to have paid off, as I saw the Dippers stallholders, whose behaviour all day had been exuberant bordering on zany, announce they were going to liven up their stall with some ball-juggling. They proceeded to descend on Betty's stall, extract a good ten balls from the bin and, taking advantage of my hastily revised sales and marketing strategy, claim a forty per cent reduction on the whole kit and caboodle. I ensured I was on hand to do the arithmetic, at the same time as listening to a harangue from Betty to the effect that the light bulb above her stall was far too weak for her to be able to read the prices of the balls, and she needed a brighter one. Not surprisingly, even the simple task of bagging up their generous haul proved a bridge too far for her, as one of the balls was seen to slip from her grasp and fall to the ground, bouncing away out of sight. Not out of sight of us, that was, but of one of the more elderly customers who failed to see the ball bounding directly into her path. A second later she slipped on it, lost her footing, and crashed heavily to the ground, nudging a nearby table and sending a plateful of Elphine's generously-filled piping hot apple turnovers, just out of the microwave, toppling over and making a forced landing on the back of her head.

Thankfully Alan was on the scene more or less immediately and decided he should personally drive her to A & E at Dellford General Hospital to attend to the resulting facial bruising and burns to the neck. "I'll leave you in charge of caretaking," he said to me. "I'm sure everything will be okay while I'm gone."

If only he had kept his mouth shut.

Barely had Alan left than my mobile rang. It was Sarah Welling from the Dellford Chronicle saying that she should be able to get someone to us by 4.40 if we were interested, but they would have to be away again by five to five. On the basis that I'd been worried the press might not be able to get there at all, I said I'd be only too pleased and issued instructions to stallholders to be dressed in beach gear in time to receive the press at the slightly earlier time. I duly made my own change, arriving back in the main hall just in time to see Betty Crabtree standing on a chair fiddling with the light bulb about which she had complained earlier. "I thought you said you'd look at this for me," she said to me accusingly. "I can't be expected to…."

She got no further, as suddenly there was a loud pop from the light fitting she was fiddling with, and the entire building was plunged into darkness. It was complete darkness, with no street lighting outside and no emergency lighting inside to mitigate the gloom. There was a collective gasp from customers, stallholders and beach party alike, and one or two screeches and wails from the children.

"The fuse box," I called out. "Where's the fuse box?"

I heard Frank's voice from across the room. "It's in the committee room," he said. "But you need a key to get into it. And Alan's the only one with a key."

It was obvious that we weren't going to be able to restore power till Alan returned, which knowing A & E at Dellford General could be any time between now and Pancake Day, so I took an instant decision to clear the hall altogether. I was frankly worried that with so much cash about the place, someone might easily make off with it under cover of darkness, or, far worse, abscond with the giant Christmas cake.

We hurried out of the building into conditions that would certainly have ruined the evening of any brass monkey that happened to be in the vicinity. As I was assisting in escorting the festive slice-laden Jemima Applecraft out of the door, I became aware of a man walking towards the building, and overheard him announcing himself as the *Dellford Chronicle* reporter and asking for me by name. Advising me that he had only limited time, he suggested that the beach party gather under the nearest street lamp for a photograph. A task easier said than done: in the Stygian gloom outside the Assembly Room it proved hard to see who was in the beach party and who wasn't, and there was also the very real dilemma of whether the customers should wait in the hope that Alan – whose mobile was switched off – would be back shortly to restore power, or whether they should get back to their firesides. Since I was now aware of something distinctly cold, flaky and snowy falling from the sky, it was no surprise to overhear the punters decide enough was enough and if they hurried they might make it home in time for the final Banker's offer on *Deal Or No Deal*. Which left just myself, the rest of the swimming costume-clad brigade, and Doris Fossett, whose sanity I had begun to doubt since her pronouncement of the weight of Elphine's cake to be twelve tons seven shillings and sixpence. Snow was now falling at such a rate that we could feel the scrunch of the accumulated flakes beneath our bare feet – I knew I'd regret the day I passed up the opportunity to invest 10p in a pair of pink size 12 flip-flops at last summer's church car boot fair – and it was with hearty relief that we dragged ourselves under the lamp post, pretended to be joyous ice-maidens whose very existences had been a preparation for this moment, and having posed for the picture, shot

WELLDIGGERS
ARMS
PUB

back to the hall looking forward to at least being able to get back into the dry.
Until we found the last person out had locked the door behind them, that is.
Three hundred yards separated us from the Welldiggers. Without thinking what other options there might have been, but merely desperate for us to congregate somewhere warm, I cried "The pub!" and with the snow continuing to swirl remorselessly round us, we sprinted down the main street, the accumulation of white globules on our bare arms and legs now turning us into extras from *The Snowman*, and arrived at the welcome main door.
Also locked.
"They open at five on Saturdays," said Mike. "Five minutes' time."
Aware that even this modest passage of the clock would stretch out like an icy eternity, there was only one thing to be done. I gave my fellow singers as good an estimation of a B flat as I could muster, together with the distinctive opening sounds "Doo be doo, tch tch tch, doo be doo, tch tch tch;" then, with snow coursing down on top of our almost naked bodies, we launched through chattering teeth into our own favourite piece. *In The Summertime When The Weather Is Hot*.
Thankfully it had its desired effect, and seconds later the door crashed open to reveal a landlord who couldn't have looked more surprised and shocked if he had opened the door to a party of pink and green spotted emus performing the *Blockbusters* Hand Jive. Seconds later we were collapsing into his bar and half a dozen whiskies later we were being furnished with our clothes by Stan. Who, complete with key to the hall and its fuse box, had been at home for the last forty minutes.
"I told Betty I'd be back from bowling by half past four," he said. "You'd have thought she might tell someone."
In the same way you'd have thought that there must be some law which prevents the free movement within the European Union of anybody with the intellectual capacity of a milk pudding.
It could have been worse. We'd made a profit. We'd had our photo taken. I'd recovered my bag of rhubarb crumble pies and triple portion of yule log intact. And nobody had run off with the giant Christmas cake. All the same, given the choice between a rerun of what I'd just lived through and summary justice at the hands of Edna Mudge's heavies, I'd in fact be more than happy to donate my lifeless body to propping up the Froggatt Street crossing of Phase 4 of the Dellford Gyratory System.

Wednesday 19th November
I never thought I'd be so pleased and privileged to sing in a fully-dressed state as I was at tonight's rehearsal.

At my suggestion, we spent most of it perfecting our choral sections for the play next Friday and Saturday. I'd spent quite a bit of time improving the lyrics and finding tunes that were rather more appropriate than those which Derek had suggested at the start, but it was all still fairly tedious going. As I pointed out to the group, though, this was good PR for us, and we might well get some more prospective members amongst those who came to watch it.
"That's a point," said Susan. "How many tickets have actually been sold for it?"
Derek looked suddenly rather uncomfortable. "We've got most of the Dellford drama group coming with their partners on Saturday," he said. "That brings us up to about forty."
"So, about half full," I said. "How about Friday?"
"Well," said Derek, "I've rung round to most people who've come to see my previous drama shows. I've left about ten messages on answering machines so hopefully they'll get back to me this week. There's about six or seven who have said they should be okay to come, another six or seven who say they'll pay on the door, and a couple of the other cast members say they're working on some of their friends and they'll let me know by Monday or Tuesday."
"So how many people have actually bought tickets and are definitely coming next Friday?" I enquired.
"Three," said Derek.

Thursday 20th November

Derek rang me at work today asking if there was any chance that I could come along to tonight's play rehearsal. "There are just one or two things I want your advice on," he said. Although we'd agreed that we wouldn't join the cast to interpose our choral bits into the play until the Sunday afternoon rehearsal, I felt duty bound to agree. After all, if we're going to be up on stage, it'll reflect badly on us as a group if the whole thing is a fiasco.
Derek told me he planned to rehearse for the first hour and a half, then deal with what he called "administrative matters" afterwards. Even though he had eight of the nine cast members with him tonight, the only absentee being Lady Wilhemina Muggleton with a throat infection, it looked just as inept as it had done when I'd last visited seven weeks ago, in fact if anything possibly more so. There were no props, no effects nor even attempts to simulate them, the acting was uniformly wooden and two of the cast were still using scripts. And even then getting their lines wrong. At ten past nine Derek called a halt, and all the cast members departed, leaving just him and me.

"I thought you said you were going to deal with administrative matters afterwards," I said.
"Er – yes," said Derek somewhat diffidently. I saw him go to a green document wallet and open it to reveal a single sheet of paper liberally sprinkled with yellow Post It notes. "I just need to remind myself what needs to be done between now and next Friday. Perhaps you could tell me what I might not have thought of."
I may have helped direct one or two productions in my student days, but among the skills I'd acquired, psychic awareness wasn't one of them. "I'm afraid I've no idea," I said. Sensing his disappointed reaction to this, I suggested I talked him through the various aspects and asked him who was attending to them.
"Lighting and scenery," I said. "Who's doing that?"
"I'll be up here all day Saturday arranging that," he said. "I'll aim to start about eightish and just keep going till I've finished."
"Publicity?"
"I'm seeing someone from the *Chronicle* tomorrow lunchtime," he replied, "and tomorrow morning I'm going round the village and round Dellford putting up posters and posting handbills. That's after I've printed them off, of course."
"Props?"
"I've made a list," he said, "and I ought to have them all ready for Sunday's rehearsal."
"Effects?"
"I need to get the wiring for those done next week," he said.
"What about the raffle and refreshments?"
"I'm having a big supermarket shop next week," he said. "I'll get all the raffle prizes and refreshments then. I'll be on the door and sell the raffle tickets as people come in. And I'll do the raffle draw in the interval after I've made the drinks."
I could hardly believe I was hearing this. "Have you not been able to delegate any of this to anyone else?" I asked incredulously.
"No, not really," Derek replied.
"And what about a prompt?" I asked. "Suppose someone forgets their lines on stage?"
"I was going to prompt," said Derek. "If I'm on stage at the time I can always whisper the line to the person who's forgotten it."
Eat your heart out, Royal Shakespeare Company.
"Just one small thing," I said. "What if you forget your own lines?"
"I won't," said Derek. "Trust me. I won't."
Except perhaps the real worry is not whether he remembers his lines but whether he remembers what he is supposed to be doing, where, when and with whom. And whether he will indeed know instinctively at any one

time if he should be in his *alter ego* as Doctor Douglas Rutherford plotting the untimely demise of Lady Wilhemina, daubing fresh layers of make-up on Eustace Rampisham's sweaty forehead, buttering slices of Tesco's Buy One Get One Free malt loaf for his loyal customers, or administering first aid to the hapless latecomer who tripped over the Dellford Amateur Dramatic Society's president's mother's outstretched wooden leg.

Sunday 23rd November

I hadn't planned to go to church this morning, but at tennish Derek rang me to say there'd been "movement" on the ticket sales front.
"Excellent," I said. "More tickets sold?"
"No," said Derek. "Less. I had three returned to me yesterday. I found them on my doormat as I got home from putting up the set. At twenty to three."
"That doesn't sound too late," I said.
"Twenty to three this morning," said Derek.
In the circumstances I decided I had no choice but to go to church and try and do some fairly robust selling myself. I'd rehearsed my sales patter pretty well, and as soon as the service finished I decided to get to work on Mrs Smiddy, deputising for Debbie at the organ. Having complimented her on her voluntary I told her she was guaranteed a first class evening's entertainment and she would basically be a fool to herself if she were even to contemplate missing out on it.
"This is Derek's play, isn't it," she said. "The play he was setting up yesterday."
"Until the small hours," I said. "That's how dedicated he is."
"I don't think so, I'm afraid," said Mrs Smiddy. "Not after what happened the last time we did a play where he was constructing the set. A scenery flat fell down during the rehearsal."
"Well, these things happen," I said. "Could have been worse."
"Not for my husband," she said. "He was supposed to be playing Henry the Fifth. After that flat hit him, he was barely up to Sixth Man."
Hardly surprisingly, the steam seemed to go out of my sales drive after that.
The rehearsal this afternoon every bit as grim as feared. Although we had the full company there, plus scenery and props, we didn't have the explosions, Derek explaining that this was "work in progress." Derek's attempts at simulating the detonations with assorted inflated paper bags and dropping to the floor *The Complete Works Of Shakespeare* – a grimly apposite choice in the circumstances – simply added to the cringeworthiness factor. Prudence Chagford, playing Lady Wilhemina Muggleton, was simply dreadful, committing the cardinal sin of

apologising every time she missed a line rather than ploughing on, and as a result the continuity was non-existent. I saw the rehearsal going on well beyond the 6.30pm finish time but fortunately we were saved by Edna Mudge arriving with a large mop which seemed to have developed its own wildlife park and demanding to know why we were still there twenty minutes after we should have gone. Certainly this generated more panic and alarm in Prudence's face than she had registered in four hours' rehearsal.
Derek emailed me the programme for my perusal tonight. I noticed that not only had he advertised that there would be a number of explosions, but stated the exact times in the action at which they would happen. "To comply with health and safety," he said. I suspect it would be far more within the spirit of health and safety legislation to warn the audience that they would be subjected throughout the play to acting of the standard of an overcooked treacle dumpling.

Wednesday 26th November

Dress rehearsal of the play tonight. Derek gathered us all together before the start and warned us that having spent all day perfecting the Christmas pudding explosions, using a remote control device, we could expect some fairly hefty bangs when the time came. As we approached the first, after twelve hideous pages littered with miscues, poor deliveries and a preponderance of no balls, we all found ourselves placing our hands in our ears and bracing ourselves for a shower of currants and glace cherries. Only for every explosive moment to pass with no effect at all on the decibel meter and without as much as one glace cherry being disturbed from its repose on the Christmas pudding on the plate in front of Lady Wilhemina Muggleton. Since this was the only aspect of the play that provided any entertainment value, the non-explosions were undoubtedly not only a blow to us but potentially hugely disappointing to the five people who'd now paid up for Friday and the drama group contingent that made up virtually all the audience for Saturday.
At my suggestion, we kept going to the end on the basis that we'd look at it afterwards – " kept going" was about as good as it got – then dismissed the cast and examined the equipment. Alexander stayed on to offer his own brand of advice and encouragement, spending some time carefully examining the wiring and the connections, picking out various tools from Derek's box and making occasional delicate adjustments which bore all the hallmarks of an expert plying his craft. Eventually he stood up and looked Derek in the eye. "I can tell you exactly what's wrong," he said.
Derek's eyes lit up for the first time that evening. "What's that?" he asked.
"It doesn't work," said Alexander.

Unfortunately I was unable to be any more helpful. So Derek's next response was to create a more elaborate wiring system which did indeed produce a most satisfying bang and a cluster of currants that eagerly leapt towards the laps of the front row of the audience. The only problem being that the wiring was so conspicuous that the potential explosive in the puddings would have been obvious to anyone giving as much as a cursory glance towards them and would probably not have gone unnoticed by the tribal warriors of the Upper Zambesi.
Derek said he needed time to work on it and come up with a few more ideas. I'm afraid that by this time I'd had enough, but tried to be as helpful as I could, referring him to the relevant pages of a manual that he'd at least had the foresight to bring with him, giving him the numbers of some local electricians, and even suggesting one or two useful Internet sites that might provide him with the clues he needed. With that, I went home and collapsed into bed.
At twenty past one in the morning the phone rang. It was Derek. "Ah," I said. "Have you achieved the breakthrough you wanted?"
"Er – I think I have," he said. "I just wanted to run it by you first."
Although barely half awake, I managed to summon sufficient reserves of mental and physical energy to enquire how he had managed to bring his technical skills to bear to master the drama's formidable pyrotechnical demands.
"Right," he said. "What do you think about just shouting BANG?"

Friday 28th November
I don't think I can ever recall dreading an evening as much as I was dreading this one. An audience of five, a cast of incompetents, and a play that depended entirely for entertainment value on special effects that were likely to be as convincing as a party political broadcast.
However, salvation – for tonight at least – was at hand. Derek phoned me just after nine this morning to say that he had decided, with great reluctance, to cancel tonight's performance, as he had found it impossible either to create sufficiently impressive effects himself or obtain the necessary assistance. However, he had managed, through his contacts in the Dellford drama group, to secure the services of a professional effects man who happened to be free and available to come over from Winchester tomorrow morning to rig up some equipment that would enable the Christmas puddings to self-destruct at the appropriate times. Although most of the profits from the production would be swallowed up simply by his petrol money – which thankfully was all he was asking for – it would at least mean the show could go on, albeit for one night only. Accordingly, Derek announced he would use tonight as an additional rehearsal to tidy up bits that hadn't gone so well on Wednesday night.

"Now I suppose I've got to ring the people I've sold tickets to for tonight, and ask them if they might be able to come tomorrow," he said. "I feel awful about letting them down."
I said that I'd be happy to do this on his behalf, thus allowing him to concentrate on making tomorrow night's performance a success, took the names of the people concerned and told him to leave it with me. He sounded almost pathetically grateful.
As I'd booked the afternoon off in anticipation of doing the play tonight I went to the Welldiggers with Katie for lunch. Stan was in there and I told him about my latest role as *de facto* publicity co-ordinator. Telling people NOT to come.
"Who are they?" asked Stan.
I produced the list from my pocket and showed it to Stan.
"Not as difficult as you thought," he said. "Arthur Sickman is dick. I mean, Arthur Dickman is sick. And his wife won't go without him. Pearl and Trevor Stanley told me the other night they'd willingly pay the admission fee all over again not to have to come. And that just leaves Kathleen Craghill. Who isn't on the phone and never answers the door."
"So how can we cancel her?"
"Oh, there's no need," said Stan. "As long as when she gets there you keep telling her the wrestling will be starting in thirty minutes she'll be quite happy."
"And when we need to leave?"
"You tell her Giant Haystacks won the final bout in the fourth round."

Saturday 29th November/Sunday 30th November
Katie and I spent most of the day in the Assembly Room watching Paul Barrowman, the effects expert, and helping Derek set up for tonight.
"I really feel sorry for him," I said. "His cast and their hangers-on haven't lifted a finger to help him."
"You're telling me," said Katie. "I overheard him talking to Paul just now. One woman apparently told him that as far as she was concerned it was all a big publicity stunt for him, she felt she had no obligation to help him feed his ego, she was there under sufferance, it was the worst play she'd ever been involved in, and once the whole sorry farce was over she'd be the first one out the door." She sipped at her mug of coffee. "And she calls herself his wife."
Although Katie had been lukewarm at first about my helping Derek as much as I had done this week, she quickly realised just how badly that help was needed. Paul heroically had all the puddings rigged up with very precise instructions to me as to how to detonate them, involving a number of remote control devices which linked into explosives concealed within a selection of Asda's finest Yuletide desserts. He'd also provided some

extra stage lighting for us and helped to improve the set. While he was doing all this, we'd been organising front-of-house aspects including programmes, refreshments and raffle, and by the end of the afternoon, the whole thing was looking – well – professional.
It wasn't till half past five that Paul said he needed to get away. He had been fantastic all day. "Just one word of advice," he said. "That last pudding. Number Four. The one that finally bumps off Lady Bugglethorpe or whatever she's called. That's a really loud bang. You're quite clear on how that's to be set?" We nodded. We'd agreed that she would enter the stage just before that particular bang, the lights would go out, and the ensuing darkness would enable her, unseen by the audience, to back off at the crucial moment. Otherwise the effect on her would, to quote Paul, be "quite dramatic."
I don't think I can ever have worked quite so hard in my life as I did during the next couple of hours. But, as I kept saying to myself, if we were able to sell our singing group to just a few of the audience it would all have been worthwhile. There were props to check off, besides the puddings for which I had been designated Chief Detonator; there was make-up to administer, although Katie fortunately was able to assist; and then there was front-of-house, welcoming in what was a very respectable-sized audience. I was too busy handing out raffle tickets to talk much about our group, but contented myself with the knowledge that there'd be ample opportunity to do so afterwards.
Among my other responsibilities was giving the official welcome and fire safety announcement, but so absorbed had I been with the front-of-house work that I realised I was late, and hurried backstage with more than a little haste, colliding heavily with Prudence, receiving some rather un-Lady Muggleton-like expletives for my pains.
At 7.28pm I hurried backstage to find Katie placing the make-up materials back into a box. "Guess who's not turned up," she said. "Ralph Pottinger. Playing Hubert Qualtrough."
I was aware that Ralph had been quite unwell earlier in the week. "Well, he hardly does anything," I said. "I could probably go on and do that part."
"Yes," said Katie, "but it means you need someone to do the second explosion. He's on stage, remember, when it happens? I mean, I'm happy to do it, if you tell me what needs doing."
I produced the remote control device which I had kept carefully in my top pocket, and had also taken care to switch off after Paul's deafeningly successful trial run. "It's very easy," I said. "The device which triggers it is the black one on this monitor.".
"Don't press it, will you," Katie implored.

"It's quite okay, it's switched off," I said. "Look. See. Switched off." I placed my finger on the black button. And pressed it.

What followed was something of a blur, and it's only now, from my bed in the Thompson Ward in Dellford General Hospital, that I've heard all the details from Katie. All would naturally have been well had my collision with Prudence not resulted in the remote device switching to the on position. All might have been well had I chosen not to have the remote pointed at the Christmas pudding on the table immediately next to me. And I think I would still have got away with it had not that pudding been the one to be used to effect Lady Muggleton's demise. But it did, I did, and it was. There followed a colossal bang, far louder than any generated by Paul during his numerous tests during the day; there was a fiery flash the impact of which knocked me to the ground; and the entire ingredients of the party-size Asda Christmas pudding were hurled into the air and descended onto my recumbent body, turning my shirtfront into a display case for Asda's executive range of assorted cherries, walnuts, sultanas, raisins and almonds with an imposing backcloth of a quarter of a ton of suet.

"Still," said Katie, "it wasn't a complete disaster."

It seemed like one to me. The start having had to be delayed by an hour and a half while the ambulance and the fire brigade arrived; losing half the audience at half time; cutting two pages to take account of missing a pudding which made a nonsense of the whole play; and by the end, the remaining audience members expressing about as much interest in joining our group as in making it to the South Pole by pogo stick on a diet of sun-dried tomatoes.

"What do you mean?" I asked weakly.

"Well," said Katie, "Derek said the reaction of the cast to the bang was the best he'd had all week. And it's prompted him to get to work on the sequel. With a summer theme and a cleverly alliterative title."

Having clung gamely to life during the last eighteen hours, I felt it ebbing away again.

"What?" I grunted miserably.

"*The Curious Case Of The Cavorting Cocktail Canapes*," said Katie.

DECEMBER

Wednesday 3rd December

After a couple of days' convalescence, I felt rather more like a human being today and duly went into work then to a rehearsal tonight. Everybody most sympathetic.

We spent some time going back over the dates and times of our various December engagements, including our visit to the High Sheriff's house next Friday the 12th (albeit only eight of us can make it), our secular carol concert on the 20th in the Assembly Room, our sacred concert on the 22nd in church, and forming a choir for the midnight service on Christmas Eve. Although Geraint wasn't present tonight, I had a letter from him which confirmed the arrangements. And Alison had a suggestion.

"Can't we ask Geraint if we can hold a crib service on Christmas Eve?" she asked. "They're a great way of getting the children in, and a lot of them probably wouldn't go at all. I'd love us to do a crib service. But there's really nothing for the children at all. Not just at Christmas. Any time."

"We used to do family services, of course," said Alan. "We gave it up when one time a quick survey of the congregation showed the youngest person there was in her forties. And she was only looking for someone to help her jump start her car."

"Well, what can you expect," said Stan, who'd popped in to lock up. "Poor Geraint's hopelessly out of touch. I mean, look at the last Christmas service he took. Kids all with their ipods and downloads, and there's Geraint asking the children – all one and a half of them – what LP's they were hoping Father Christmas would bring them."

"It could have been worse," said Mark.

"It got worse," said Stan. "When he said he was hoping for Arthur Daley's *Rock Around The Cock.*"

Friday 5th December

After Wednesday's meeting, in which we all agreed it would be great to do the crib service, I'd rung Geraint about the possibility, making the point that Alison had made about lack of things for the children. He'd told us that he was willing to give it a go, but asked me if, perhaps with Alison's support, I could promote it around the village as he said he just didn't have the time. I said I'd be happy to do whatever was necessary. Obviously there was something of an ulterior motive, in that it'll give us a chance to showcase our talents as a singing group amongst people who might not have been attracted by any of our events so far. But it would be so nice to get some younger people into church – after all, if we don't, there won't be a congregation of any description in twenty years' time –

and this might be the ideal basis for greater family involvement and more young people in the church in the New Year.
I phoned Alison who said she'd be delighted to help me. We agreed on a vigorous advertising campaign in church and a leaflet drop in the village, and we decided we had nothing to lose by contacting the *Chronicle*. Even if we did end up as an afterthought in the Spadger column underneath the report of the discovery of a rogue frozen pea amongst the roast parsnips in the Christmas dinner delivered by Meals on Wheels to Charmaine Doubleday of Throgmorton Drive.
Geraint rang later to ask if we had in mind a time for the crib service to start. I told him I thought that early evening was best, say 5pm, particularly as some parents might well be working on Christmas Eve. I said I also thought there was something rather magical about a Christmas Eve service in the declining light, with heightened anticipation of the excitement of the day ahead and the congregation exiting from the church under a starlit sky calling to mind the mystic magic of the first Nativity two thousand years ago.
"Er – yes, yes," said Geraint after a few moments' silence. "I suppose you're right. I had rather thought it might work better earlier in the day, but….no, no….five o'clock it is." He sounded rather fed up.
I mentioned to Stan later that I was rather surprised at Geraint's rather cool reaction to my suggestion of the 5pm start. "Do you know of any major spiritual or theological reason against it?" I asked him.
"Absolutely," said Stan. "UK Gold are screening an *On The Buses* quadruple bill starting at 4.30."

Sunday 7th December
Wasted no time after a singularly speedy service – Geraint was anxious to finish early so he could get off to the Retford And District Traction Company Old Boys' Club's Christmas knees-up – in drumming up support for the crib service, starting with a snowy-haired woman three rows back who had two youngsters with her.
"Tell me," I said, "would you like to come to the crib service with your grandchildren?"
"I haven't any grandchildren," she snapped. "These are my own children. Well, two of them, anyway."
I did my best to retrieve the situation.
"I'm so sorry, " I said, "but we'd love to see you and all your family at the crib service, anyway."
"That may be difficult," she said. "My eldest will be away, I'm afraid."
"Somewhere nice, I trust?" I asked.
"Pentonville," she replied.

Wednesday 10th December

A busy day. It got off to a bad start when, forced to drive to work because of a couple of meetings I had later today, I found myself in a horrendous jam on the ring road system and just sat there for over 45 minutes. I switched on local radio and was told the town had been brought to a standstill by a group calling itself Justice For Archie or the JFA's. When at last the police intervened and I made it into work, I found that they were protesting about the arrest and detention of an illegal immigrant (actually Mbangwanga Areche so one can understand the use of an English corruption of his surname) who is facing deportation back to his home country; if he is deported, he will be immediately thrown in jail and in all probability executed for high treason. It certainly put into perspective my annoyance at arriving at work to find the only milk left in the fridge was two days past its Use By date, but it certainly is very gloomifying to note that the JFA's plan a campaign of "massive disruption" in Dellford during the run-up to Christmas.

I emailed the High Sheriff's secretary after lunch to confirm arrangements for Friday. She advised me that he's out of the country until Friday morning but will look forward to meeting us on the front steps of his home at just before 7.15pm, after which we will serenade the arriving guests over the next 30 minutes. We will then depart and receive a generous cheque to be divided between a chosen charity and our own group funds.

It was good to get that sorted out, but another aggravation awaited me tonight when, on arrival at the Assembly Room for our rehearsal, which I'd called for 7pm instead of the usual 7.30pm, I saw three elderly women sitting round a table in the main hall, engaged in obviously detailed discussion.

They looked up at me suspiciously as I approached them. "Can I help you?" one of them demanded. She sounded like a belligerent farmer who'd caught schoolchildren trespassing in one of her fields.

"Yes," I said. "We've a meeting here this evening. We've booked the room."

"When for?"

"I asked Mrs Crabtree to book it for seven," I said. I blamed myself. I should have known that six phone calls and two written reminders would be nowhere near enough. To make it worse, I noticed other members of our group were arriving and pulling up chairs in readiness for a prompt start.

"This is the inaugural meeting of our new Netley Road Neighbourhood Watch scheme and accordingly is extremely important," the woman said, looking at me over the top of her spectacles that sat awkwardly halfway down her nose. Her voice heavy with irony, she went on "But obviously

your group is far more important so I suppose we'll just have to adjourn. 7th January, 5.30pm, please, ladies."
With very bad grace she began to gather up her pile of papers and donned a suede purple hat that sat on the table beside her. She then got up to leave, and motioned to her colleagues to do the same. While they were doing that, and then making what seemed to be a painfully lengthy departure, I called the group together and announced arrangements for convening at the High Sheriff's house on Friday evening. But when ten minutes later the three of them were still engaged in conversation in the corner of the room I said we must make a start with what I liked to call our warm-up piece. This was a work called *African Carol,* a really full-blooded powerful celebration of the Nativity which I'd found on the Internet last month and which we're going to sing in our sacred carol concert. Four pages of vigorous Swahili chanting at triple *forte* later, the would-be guardians of law and order in Netley Road had finally been frightened off and we were able to enjoy an excellent rehearsal.
I did however feel a pang of conscience about disrupting the ladies in their valuable community work and as Stan came along to lock up, I shared my concern with him.
"I wouldn't worry about it," he said. "They've been talking about setting up a Neighbourhood Watch since 1980. Never happens. It's just an excuse for them to have a gossip and a moan. Was the lady with the purple hat there?"
I nodded.
"Thought so," said Stan. "Norah Spottiswoode. A tough old cookie. Doesn't suffer fools. There was a burglary in her road a few years back. She happened to witness it. She was terrifying. Scared him absolutely rigid. Told him he was a brainless imbecile who was a disgrace to his community and the sooner he went off and did something useful with his life, the better. Reduced him to jelly. He was virtually in tears. He ran off and vowed to chuck in his activities from that moment."
"And did he?"
"Yes, he did," said Stan. "Pity, really. Finest Detective Chief Superintendent we've ever had."

Friday 12th December

Was woken up by very high winds and rain, and when I switched on the local radio I heard that apparently we were in the middle of one of the worst storms in the past decade. Somehow I struggled into work, but it seemed that others weren't so lucky with their journeys; all the region's airports had been brought to a virtual standstill, many roads were shut and train services were severely disrupted.

Remembering that the High Sheriff's secretary had advised me that he would be out of the country till this morning, I rang her to check that all was still well for tonight and he would indeed be back in time for his function to take place. Unfortunately it seemed she hadn't made it in either, so I phoned the High Sheriff's home address. If I tried the line once, I tried it twenty times; either it was engaged, or nobody answered. Exasperated, I decided on one last go and amazingly this time I got through.

"High Sheriff's residence," a man answered.

"Hallo," I said, "just ringing to check that the dinner for tonight is still going on. And that he is still expecting our little deputation as everyone is arriving."

"Little deputation, uh?" he echoed.

"That's right," I said. "We'll be there from 7.15 – about eight of us in all. Maybe a few hangers-on. We don't intend to outstay our welcome. But we like to think we'll make an impact on the evening."

"Oh, right," he said. "Well, thanks for letting us know."

I thought that was a rather peculiar comment. "Didn't you know we were coming?" I queried.

"No," he said. "I just came in to deliver a crate of turnips."

I honestly give up.

The storm abated during the afternoon and having checked with the others, we agreed that we would go along anyway, reckoning that if the High Sheriff had been delayed and decided to cancel the function, we wouldn't have had far to travel anyway. And we might be a crate of turnips better off.

Although Mark and Susan were running late, the rest of us arrived in convoy at ten past seven. I'd never been to the High Sheriff's house before but it certainly was a magnificent eighteenth century mansion in extensive grounds; there was a lovely festive atmosphere with coloured lamps illuminating the stone steps leading up to the front door, lights blazing in the entrance hall, and a fragrance of burning wood in the now starry and crisp night air. It was like something from a Jane Austen novel. The only slight problem was the absence of the High Sheriff to greet us.

I took an executive decision that we should ring the bell to announce ourselves, and in the meantime those of us who'd arrived could warm up with the *African Carol*. The timing was perfect, for as we began singing, three cars arrived in rapid succession. Two of them, I noticed, were police cars, from which a total of five uniformed officers exited and made their way purposefully towards the entrance. I knew from what Charlie had told me that the High Sheriff had a very close working relationship with the Chief Constable, so I wasn't at all surprised that the local force was well represented at the function tonight. What did rather surprise me, as

we embarked on the women-only section at the start of page three, was the officers marching up to us, yelling at us to stop singing, and producing a generous supply of handcuffs.
"We've had two separate pieces of information that members of a group named Justice For Archie, campaigning on behalf of a suspected illegal immigrant, would be attending to disrupt the function taking place here tonight," said one of them. "Accordingly, we have reason to apprehend a breach of the peace and you're all under arrest."
"Oh, for goodness sake," Alan protested. "We're here to sing carols for the High Sheriff."
"Apparently Archie's native country is Sudan," said the officer. "And although I'm no expert, what you were singing sounded distinctly African. I mean, it's not God Help Us Merry Gentlemen, is it? You're all under arrest."
And moments later, having been informed that it might harm our defence if we did not mention something we might later rely on in court, we were being given a free ride into town.
Fortunately after an hour and a half in Dellford Police Station, and a plastic cup of Diesel oil from the vending machine in the reception area, the police were finally convinced that the available evidence pointed to their having made a mistake. Little things like our producing for forensic examination folders containing all the music we were planning to sing had we had the chance. Like the High Sheriff appearing in person, having arrived home 15 minutes after we'd been carted off, threatening the officers with action for unlawful arrest, wrongful imprisonment and forcible deprivation of pre-prandial seasonal entertainment. And the fact that information was received that the real Justice For Archie group had in fact been disrupting the Mayor of Dellford's Christmas party at Dellford Town Hall by throwing rotten eggs and rancid tomatoes at the Shipton Under Wychwood And District Steel Band. But it was probably dear Jim who saved us, by telling the police he never watched the news anyway and said the only Archie he knew was a member of an American pop group. That topped the charts in 1969 with *Sugar Sugar*.

Sunday 14th December

Geraint decided it was about time for another "getting to know you" session at church this morning. I turned to the elegantly-dressed lady behind me and said "I don't think we've met."
"I think you'll find we have," she said. "When we did this before. Twice."
Anyway she was good enough to take one of the leaflets on which we've advertised not only the crib service but our two carol services over the next nine days. And after the excellent Christmas carvery lunch at the

Welldiggers, we set off to do a village leaflet drop, Alan and Jim making up one team and Alison and myself the other. We decided that although it would notionally be quicker to do it individually, it'd be pleasanter to work in pairs and we'd see how we were doing after a couple of hours. In fact we weren't a pair for long, as Alison had a friend staying with her named Nikki who decided to come along as well and who proved to be excellent company.

"You know," said Nikki after we'd polished off a few streets with remarkable speed, "I think it would be good to actually chat to some of these people as we go. Knock on a few doors. Explain what we're doing."

"Won't some people find that a bit intrusive?" I queried.

"Possibly," said Nikki, "but as a Christian I would rather be held to account for intrusiveness than not caring."

I couldn't really argue with that one. Not at that stage anyway. But after two and a quarter hours of having been threatened with everything from the business end of a shotgun to Mavis Cantwell's Cornish holiday photographs, and being told by at least six households that they had already happily been converted to Jehovah's Witnesses and they didn't want another lecture on the subject thank you very much, I couldn't help wondering if not caring was the better option. And I was beginning to positively yearn for my pot of decaf Yorkshire tea and slice of Sainsbury's economy iced fruit bar as we began to trudge up our final street, and knocked on the door of number 153A. For the umpteenth time that afternoon we explained the different services and asked which one suited the resident in question.

"What's meant by secular?" the elderly man asked suspiciously.

"We mean carols that aren't based on religious premise," I said. "Songs about eating and drinking, making merry, that sort of thing. Do you know what I mean by a wassail?"

The man pondered for a few moments. "I may be interested in that," he said. "Very interested."

For the first time that afternoon, I felt I was actually getting through to someone.

"So what more would you like to know about it?" I asked.

"Well," he replied, "what's a woss and what sort of reductions are you offering?"

Saturday 20th December

It had certainly been a busy week. Before Wednesday's rehearsal I'd got a call from a Ricky Hardaway-Fishwicks saying that he'd heard all about our group and our carol concert tonight and could he record one of our carols to go out during the run-up to Christmas on Love It FM, the local radio station I'd appeared on in March. He'd asked if we could do the

recording on Friday afternoon, but with only a handful of the membership available, we had to abandon that idea. We agreed instead that he'd come to the Assembly Room this evening when we could do it immediately before our secular concert.
Then at the rehearsal itself a problem had arisen. Namely, that nobody on our rounds had expressed the slightest interest in the sacred carol service and everyone Alan and Jim had spoken to confirmed that while they fancied the secular concert or the crib service, sitting in a cold church for a couple of hours on top of that was a bridge too far. After a long discussion we'd taken a deep breath and agreed to cancel the sacred carol service and ensure that all the music from it was incorporated somehow into the other three events. It was certainly disappointing to have had to take time out on the Thursday to let everybody know, but with no immediate evidence, when I arrived back in the village this evening, of mass demonstrations or the presence of riot police on the streets, I reckoned we had probably got this one right.
Anyway, having spent all last night and much of today working out the revised running order for tonight's carol concert in the Assembly Room, I made my way along there this evening feeling really positive about the programme we had planned. A happy mix of sacred and secular, not too lengthy, and an interval with a goodly spread of Christmas fare which Elphine had worked through the night to prepare. We had also built in some breaks for the choir which would be filled with some cello music from a work friend of Frank's named Norma Carrisford and some seasonal readings from one Bernard Cadogan who was one of our house-to-house "victims" from last Sunday afternoon. I'd agreed to meet Norma and Bernard at ten to seven to talk them through their items, then Ricky Hardaway-Fishwicks was due at seven for the recording which we needed to do before the audience started coming in. But even this ostensibly straightforward itinerary was blown to smithereens when my mobile rang just before six fifty. It was Ricky.
"Slight change of plan," he said. "I'm not going to be able to make it."
I told him I was sorry to hear it, but to be frank I wasn't too devastated as I'd been concerned about getting the recording completed in time.
"Anyway," he continued. "Don't despair, because two of my colleagues are on their way. They'll be with you as soon as they can."
"It's going to be a bit tricky," I said. "We're starting our concert in forty minutes."
"They've come a long way to do this for you," said Ricky.
"From the Love It FM studio at Markbury, you mean?" I asked.
"Bit further than that," said Ricky.
"How far?" I enquired.
"Naples," said Ricky.

I was assured they were "close by" which I assumed meant on this side of the English Channel, but Ricky seemed a little reluctant to specify a time. He was able to give me a mobile phone number but having tried it twelve times and left six increasingly frantic voicemail messages I was really still none the wiser as to whether they were tearing up the Dellford ring-road, having their bags searched at Bournemouth Airport, or sitting in the video lounge on the Cherbourg-Weymouth ferry supping duty-free Carlsberg in front of *The Shawshank Redemption.* By now the punters had not only made their way in but had made themselves comfortable and a hush had descended over the hall, in anticipation of a prompt start and a countdown to the hot fruit punch and Elphine's rich fruit cake. There was no time to convene an emergency committee meeting. We'd just have to get on with the concert.
Then, at 7.29, there was an explosion of sound from the back of the hall. Two men duly appeared, armed with various bags and cases, and announced themselves as the Ricky substitutes. "Sorry we're late," one of them said. "We'd have been here twenty minutes ago but our phone kept ringing then cutting out before we could pull off the road to answer. Some total nutter."
"We're just about to start," I said. "Can you wait till the interval?"
"Difficult," said the taller of the two. "We're going on somewhere else straight after this. I promise it won't take long. Half an hour for the whole shooting match. Just give us ten minutes to set up, we'll be out of here before you know it."
I considered the options quickly. The idea of a ten-minute first half, an interval for the recording, and then a 90-minute second half wasn't immediately appealing. But telling them they'd forsaken the *dolce vita* on the sun-kissed shores of the Mediterranean for no good reason appealed to me even less. So I took a deep breath, explained to the audience that there'd be a slight delay, and hustled the travel-weary recording crew out to the committee room, fortified by assurances from the duo that they'd definitely be no longer than thirty minutes. In fact the shorter of the two was prepared to stake his mother's life on it.
If his mother wasn't worried by this promise, I can only say that after five attempts at recording the chosen piece, each one frustrated by musical errors, technical problems or background noise, she perhaps needed to be. And after our twelfth go at it, which we agreed would have to be our last even if it resembled less *Deck The Hall With Boughs of Holly* than *Who Do You Think You Are Kidding Mister Hitler*, I was already making a mental note to ring her and suggest she blew the dust off her life insurance policy.
All the time, reports of the mood of the natives had been filtering back – indeed it was the crash of the door of the committee room with the first

report which had been responsible for the failure of an otherwise unblemished fourth recording – and the news was not good. What had started as good-humoured acceptance evolved steadily into phlegmatic British stoicism, metamorphosing gently into mild irritation, changing at Clapham Junction into extreme annoyance, and just minutes now appeared to separate us from the need to don tin hats in defence against the first volley of Elphine's chicken vol-au-vents. So rather than wait for the punters to hurl them at us, we decided it might be best if they ate them instead. In between gulps of hot punch I undertook a hasty rewrite of the whole programme, condensing the cello and reader sections and losing some of the less exciting pieces. I felt confident that, all being well, we would still have our audience away in good time, and get the chance to publicise our group and possibly recruit some new members too.

The only problem was that I still had not had the chance to meet with Norma or Bernard and consider the length and content of their input.

Initially things went well. With stomachs full of seasonal food and drink there was definitely a sense of reconciliation and forgiveness in the air, and our first group of items earned a huge round of generous applause. Then came Norma the cellist. Just watching her set up did not give me huge confidence that we were about to witness a master craftswoman at work, and the five minutes it took her to get in tune with Debbie on keyboard was long enough to provoke a worrying number of glazed eyes amongst the cash customers. The first four pages were tolerable, but enthusiasm for the piece was definitely waning after the next half dozen, and Norma perhaps sensibly decided to get herself to the end of the work as quickly as possible. It was just a shame that she hadn't told Debbie that her idea of doing this was to up the tempo from *andante moderato* to *molto prestissimissimissimo*, confidently cruising to page fourteen whilst Debbie was still meandering three pages behind, the cellist eventually motoring past the finishing post as the hapless accompanist yielded to her rival's superior engine power and crawled self-consciously into the pits for a much-needed oil change.

A robust rendition of group two of our musical programme saw a slight mellowing of the atmosphere, but that was before Bernard Cadogan took to the floor. It's difficult to put into words the impact of his rendition on my consciousness, but before very long I can only say that had I had been offered a choice between listening to him for another 30 seconds or being made to stay an entire weekend with my Uncle Ernest going through his complete collection of snaps accumulated during 23 consecutive years' holidaying at Clacton-on-Sea with his sister Deirdre, I'd have been straight onto the Internet checking out train times to Bradford North. Once again, the expressions on the faces of the audience were instructive to say the least. To begin with, happy anticipation of a pithy seasonal anecdote or extract from the great works of Hardy or Dickens. After five minutes of home-produced musings on Christmases past in the Cadogan household, polite and indulgent amusement. After ten more minutes of same, mild irritation mingled with desultory sighing, a pinch of unrest, a sprinkling of teeth clicking, and two level teaspoonfuls of foot tapping. And with thirty minutes on the clock, Bernard now holding forth on Christmas 1895 in Epping as seen through the eyes of his great-grandfather's sister's doctor's undertaker Albert, into this uncomfortably rich mixture of ingredients were added a cluster of yawns and an unusually keen interest on the part of the assembled company in the faces of their watches and the contents of their earlobes.

Aware that what I was about to do would remove me from Bernard's Christmas card list until the year 2035 at the earliest, as well as have me blackballed from the Epping Local History Society for probably another few decades after that, I waited until Bernard paused for breath, just at the point at which Albert had begun to pluck the feathers off the family Christmas goose, and hurried forward. "Thank you very much, Bernard," I said. "Time now for some more music, I think." I detected a slightly crestfallen expression on his face, but I would sooner have fielded a downpour of crests than risk being lynched by a ruthless mob whose frustrated and angry expressions seemed certain to be translated any moment into bloody and destructive vengeance. And that was just the rest of the choir.

With the time now at 10.40pm, I indicated that we should move briskly to the final section of the programme and we duly did so, reeling off what would have been, had all gone according to plan, a happy and suitably festive finale to our concert, and cue for another bout of conviviality over the remains of the punch and canapés. As it was, I don't think I can remember a room clearing so fast since my fifth form maths lesson when the sound of the fire alarm mercifully cut off Mr Snagsby in the middle of his binomial coefficients.

Sunday 21st December

We treated ourselves to a long lie-in this morning. Katie, who had not felt up to coming out last night, was still feeling off colour today, and the last place I wanted to be was at church finding some new way of reducing my standing in the community even further below the level of a sackful of pureed elephant droppings.

My penance for this piece of indolence was a telephone call from Ricky.

"Just heard the recording," he said. "Absolutely thrilled with it. Many thanks."

I told him it was a pleasure. Through gritted teeth.

“We didn’t discuss the amount of the fee we should pay you,” said Ricky, “and we wondered if you had a figure in mind.”
I told him I’d not really thought about it, but the group could certainly do with the money, and we’d discuss it and get back to him. I told him I was more concerned about the complete fiasco that last night’s concert had been, entirely as a result of the recording, but perhaps being heard over the Love It FM airwaves would make up for that.
“So when will we hear ourselves on air?” I asked.
“Depends on the air time they’ve paid for,” said Ricky. “I don’t really deal with that side of things, I’m afraid.”
“What do you mean, paid for?” I queried.
“Oh, didn’t we tell you?” said Ricky. “I thought I had. I’m from Fishwicks, the advertising agency. Your carol’s going to be used in adverts for Hambleton and Sons.”
“And what’s their line of business?” I enquired.
“Drain and sewer blockages,” said Ricky.
So after a year of my trying to promote the Lambsball Green Singers as a reputable and vibrant part of the area’s musical scene, this was how we were showing ourselves off to the local populace. A brief snatch of *Deck The Hall With Boughs Of Holly* underneath a telephone number for same-day cesspit clearance.

Wednesday 24th December – Christmas Eve

Despite the anticipatory wonder and excitement that is traditionally associated with Christmas Eve, I couldn’t have felt less happily disposed towards this particular day if the doorbell had rung to reveal a quartet of Daleks bearing a demand for payment of an overdue water bill.
Then, at nine thirty or so, the phone rang. “Hi,” said a young female voice. “This is Sarah Hemsby from Love It FM. The phone’s been going mental this morning. Everybody wants to know who that super choir are that feature in the Hambleton advert. They want to know when they can hear you and whether you’re doing anything special over the Christmas period.”
It was the work of a moment to tell her to invite all their listeners to the Church of St Augustine, Lambsball Green, at 5pm this evening for the crib service.
It took slightly longer to ring all the members of the group to tell them whatever else they had planned for 1700 tonight, whether it was a flight to Lapland, an attack of bubonic plague or a stiff whisky in front of the *Police Camera Action* Celebrity Christmas Special, all leave was cancelled and personnel were to report to church vestry HQ for sealed orders at 1636 hours. And another few moments to detail Elphine to corner Dellford’s entire supplies of mincemeat, marzipan, flour and

margarine and shut herself in her kitchen for the ensuing six and a half hours.
But it was worth it. The whole service was a triumph. Regulars at St Augustine's said they'd never seen so many people in the church since the funeral of the universally disliked Major Bartholomew Cotherstone-Pilbrow MA,KCMG,DSO. And most of those had only turned up to satisfy themselves he really was dead. Even 15 minutes before the start there was standing room only, with calls to pass further down the cars, and stentorian announcements from officials about the need for northbound passengers to change at Finsbury Park. Geraint with his sermon earned the respect, affection and support of the entire congregation – by not actually preaching a sermon. The singing was tremendous and our rendition of *Deck The Hall*, inserted at the last moment by popular demand, received enthusiastic requests for an encore, many of the punters saying it benefited hugely from not being drowned by the words "Blocked Drain? No strain" in lazy Cockney drawl. The duration of the service, at 28 minutes 27 seconds, was almost immediately being eagerly scrutinised and debated on worldwide Internet sites by religious historians as a possibly unprecedented and unique example of an act of Christian worship that left the congregation wanting more. And Elphine's festive slices, which had been so rapturously received at our fayre last month, flew off the plates so fast that we were left wondering if she'd coated them not only with sugared almonds but wings and Rolls Royce engines.
I walked home feeling that that one service had justified all my hard work over the last year. Only one thing saddened me: that Katie, who, bless her, had been so supportive and understanding of me throughout the year, had again not felt up to coming and witnessing it all for herself, preferring just to go out for a short walk to clear her head. Yet when I greeted her tonight as I arrived home, she looked beautiful. Quite beautiful. It wasn't just that she was attractively made up and stunningly dressed in a deep red jumper, tight jeans and long black boots. There was a serene joy in her eyes I'd never seen before, even when I'd asked her to be my wife exactly five years ago. And as I looked deeper into her eyes, I detected not only joy but a sense of real excitement which went well beyond the traditional Christmas Eve anticipation.
"I just thought you ought to know," she said with a smile. "I'm pregnant."
And there was I thinking that it couldn't get any better than straphanging in the aisles and Elphine's jet-propelled traybakes.
Among the many people I had to ring to share the wonderful news, I felt I must call Geraint and thank him for agreeing to hold such a fantastically successful crib service.

"Yes," he said. "I only hope the midnight service isn't an awful anticlimax."
In other circumstances I'd have fervently shared his hopes. But as I write, with an hour to go before that service, I wouldn't really be too bothered if thirty minutes prior to the start a rogue number 78A Glasgow to Kirkintilloch bus filled with a potent cocktail of potting compost and toxic waste swerved across the road to avoid a shower of frozen hake pieces thrown by the Lambsball Green Dippers and smashed into the lychgate completely blocking the entrance to the church for the six people intending to go to the service that were left following Betty Crabtree's announcement that the service was to be relocated in the St Ignatius Community Centre, Cornmarket Street, Cheadle.

Wednesday 31st December

The period between Christmas and New Year can often be a bit of a let-down, but not for me this year. In a burst of confidence following the momentous events of Christmas Eve, I'd spent quite a bit of last Saturday morning ringing round the many people who'd expressed an interest in joining the group at the fayre on 15th November and of course following the crib service on Christmas Eve. It turned out that most were free on New Year's Eve so, bizarrely, we found ourselves in the Assembly Room today doing voice tests. Alan and I reasoned that it would be great to start the New Year with a few extra singers and we'd have that bit more time to plan the spring programme, knowing how many voices we'd have available to us.
A bad start, with Edna Mudge storming in demanding to know who was responsible for "fouling up the waterworks." Unfortunately although there were no eye-witnesses, it was clear from what she went on to say that there was ample material, albeit circumstantial in nature, tending to prove beyond reasonable doubt that there was a connection between the incident in question and our concert eleven days previously. The fact that a piece of sheet music was involved was particularly powerful evidence for the prosecution. I indicated that I would convene a hearing at the earliest opportunity, expedite the service of process to bring the alleged offender or offenders to justice, and do my best to find a decent-fitting black cap.
And so to the voice tests. Of 26 people who said they'd be there, Alan predicted fifteen would turn up and told me to be satisfied with twelve. We ended up with ten. The first two didn't have great voices but they were very nice people and I think it was that, combined with a fear that we wouldn't find anyone else that morning, which persuaded us to let them in. There followed what could only be described as a sea of mediocrity with occasional islands of sheer awfulness. Finally, right at

the end of a long and frustrating morning, a balding man in his late sixties with a slight stutter came forward. He told us that he "really wanted this.....it would mean so much to me if I were to have this opportunity" – Alan asked me in a rather loud whisper if he'd been watching too much *X Factor* – and with a trembling hand, produced from his pocket a crumpled-up sheet of music which he slowly and very deliberately proceeded to unfold. He put on a pair of dark brown spectacles, looked expectantly at Debbie at the keyboard, and a tense hush descended on the room as the introductory music came to an end and, with a deep breath, he opened his mouth to sing.

And he was even worse than all the others.

Still, the morning hadn't been a total disaster. We had two singers with a degree of promise, both delightful people. Both, more importantly, were in their forties, and their inclusion alone will provide our group with a higher percentage of those in the under-50 bracket than at least two thirds of the choirs I've been in since leaving college.

Afterwards we all adjourned to the Welldiggers for a pub lunch, joined by some of those who'd helped or hindered us during the year. Jonathan popped in briefly then made his excuses, saying his Black Berry was on the blink and he needed to make further inroads into the six hundred and thirty-four emails that he'd found this morning had accumulated in his in box since he'd last been in work.....on Sunday afternoon. Betty was there: she'd finally had mercy on us and decided we should no longer benefit from her own brand of organisational skill, rumour having it that she'd obtained an executive position within Traffic Control HQ on the M25. Charlie came up and said hallo, charitably telling us following our radio ad that if we wanted to cheapen our image still further he happened to know that Fishwicks had just agreed to take on the advertising for Woodard, Grimble and Schluck, solicitors with an unusual penchant for ambulance chasing. There was Angus, or Splungeworks as Charlie tipsily called him today, promising our crib service triumph a couple of lines in his first column of the New Year, latest developments in the breaking news story of the Phantom Cycle Clip Pincher of Corbett Rise permitting. And Derek came up and said that he'd now formulated his New Year project, departing from his traditional specialist skills as a playwright to turn his hand to general fiction in the form of a comic novel about a cowboy builder – coincidentally also named Derek – and the efforts made by his disgruntled customers to obtain some civil redress. *Hand Del's Mess Higher.*

But despite – or perhaps even because of – their input, we agreed that there was much to celebrate, and even more to look forward to. Elphine's treats, sweet and savoury. The offer of at least three concerts in the New Year, all of them in quite prestigious locations. The possibility, mooted

by Alan, of some recording with a view to a CD or even a DVD. The virtual guarantee of sufficient interest and funds for a French tour in the spring. And, just as important as all of these things, the thrill of being part of a friendly, competent, enthusiastic and growing complement of singers capable of giving immense pleasure to listeners, raising money for good causes, and bringing our local community together with a real sense of common purpose.
First, though, I need to look in my local directory. For someone capable of unjamming the Little Drummer Boy from the ladies' bog.